Yoga & Sadhana

Author
Dr. Satya Pal
Dholan Dass Aggarwal
Yoga Specialists and Naturopaths

Translated by
Shri G.L. Anand
Editor NCERT, New Delhi

&

Gp. Capt. B.S. Bakhshi

PUSTAK MAHAL®
DELHI • MUMBAI • BANGALORE • PATNA • HYDERABAD

Publishers

Pustak Mahal®, Delhi-110006

Sales Centres

- 6686, Khari Baoli, Delhi-110006, *Ph:* 23944314, 23911979
- 10-B, Netaji Subhash Marg, Daryaganj, New Delhi-110002
  Ph: 23268292, 23268293, 23279900 • *Fax:* 011-23280567
  E-mail: rapidexdelhi@indiatimes.com

Administrative Office

J-3/16 (Opp. Happy School), Daryaganj, New Delhi-110002
Ph: 23276539, 23272783, 23272784 • *Fax:* 011-23260518
E-mail: info@pustakmahal.com • *Website:* www.pustakmahal.com

Branch Offices

BANGALORE: 22/2, Mission Road (Shama Rao's Compound),
Bangalore-560027, *Ph:* 22234025 • *Fax:* 080-22240209
E-mail: pmblr@sancharnet.in • pustak@sancharnet.in

MUMBAI: 23-25, Zaoba Wadi (Opp. VIP Showroom), Thakurdwar,
Mumbai-400002, *Ph:* 22010941 • *Fax:* 022-22053387
E-mail: rapidex@bom5.vsnl.net.in

PATNA: Khemka House, 1st Floor (Opp. Women's Hospital), Ashok
Rajpath, Patna-800004 , *Ph:* 3094193 • *Telefax:* 0612-2302719
E-mail: rapidexptn@rediffmail.com

HYDERABAD: 5-1-707/1, Brij Bhawan, Bank Street, Koti,
Hyderabad-500095, *Telefax:* 040-24737290
E-mail: pustakmahalhyd@yahoo.co.in

© Pustak Mahal, 6686, Khari Baoli, Delhi-110006

ISBN 81-223-0092-8

6th Edition : December 2004

Printed at : Param Offsetters, Okhla, New Delhi-110020

Contents

Preface

Yoga is a way of life and enables us to have multi dimensional approach to life. The human body is not the aim of yoga but is considered means of going beyond physical form of body. Unbalanced state of cause and effect result in ill health. Equilibrium of two is the basic aim of Yoga. A healthy body, therefore may be called as the foundation of Yoga.

Yoga is both an art and science. It can alone save the modern man from personal determination and circumstantial frustration. In other words the practice of 'Yoga' postulates keeping the body healthy and the mind calm and peaceful. Health is our birth-right, and to remain healthy, it is not necessary to depend upon any health centre, physician or medication. It is entirely in our hands to keep healthy. However, in the present-day conditions keeping good health is becoming more and more difficult, and diseases are proliferating. All sorts of evils have crept into our society. Utter selfishness, cut-throat competition, murders, communal riots, rampant corruption—all these are attributable to the progressive degeneration of the human body and mind. Certain yogic principles have to be observed for maintaining sound health. If we follow these principles and regularly practice Yoga and Yogasanas it would not be a problem to enjoy full strength and vigour.

Healthy means to know our inner self. It signifies equilibrium and self-control. If there is a key to life, it is Yoga. Our energy gets drained in the search for materialistic comforts. The whole atmosphere today is surcharged with tension and various types of pollution. We tend to blame the elements for our physical disorders and mental tension. If we catch a bad cold or fever, we blame it on the weather forgetting that the whole process of health generates from within ourselves. Nature has made our physical structure perfect and complete and invested this mechanism with the capability of keeping itself in good health. If any foreign matter sneaks into our body and gets stuck up there, we call it 'disease'. All the present and future ailments can be ascribed to this factor. It we take reasonably good care of our body and do not let any harmful matter remain inside, we shall never fall ill. Yogasanas are extremely beneficial in this respect. The science of Yoga is the science of Cosmos. The Yogic Art is Cosmic Art. When you achieve Yoga, you find pure consciousness in action and good health, resistance power, etc. When the heart works normally through the circulation of blood, it gets the blood purified by the lungs and keeps the digestive system in order; the various glands function and maintain the balance of body; and the mind works calmly and keeps the body functioning through the intricate nervous system. In case of illness it does become inevitable to resort to medication, but health is regained only through the intrinsic strength of the inner organs. Medicine helps when the body mechanism functions properly.

If medicine could by itself give health, man could remain healthy, especially now when science has made incredible strides and medicines have been discovered for all sorts of diseases, and new techniques of treatment have been evolved. But this has not happened: diseases have proliferated and the mind has become more and more miserable. Increasing dependence of man on medicine is, therefore, counter-productive.

This, however, is not to say that immense benefits cannot be derived for scientific innovations and new methods of treatment. All that is needed is that we look within, and with a little introspection learn that it is only through the natural ways like the Yogic exercises, regulated life-style, etc., that we can keep ourselves in fine shape.

Yoga is a great dynamo of power which you have to tap to become a master of yourself and the world. The greatest power and energy is within you, not without you. Yoga is fully capable of giving the humanity physical and mental health. When one is sound of mind and body, one is one's own self. And when we are the master of ourselves, we do not have to indulge in vices like deception, vulgarity or obscenity or telling lies. Indeed, we can maintain serenity even under the worst kind of provocation.

It is the considerations that have motivated the writing of this book. This book is the product of 40 years of constant practice and experience of Yoga, and has been written with the desire to show the world the way to healthy body, mind and soul. The main aim of writing this book is to present Yoga Techniques to the ordinary people in the simple language. It provides maximum information in straightforward, simple and short form. Service to the mankind is the inspiration behind this book. It fills the vacuum of such a good book on Yoga, which is in the easy reach of common man.

In order that this book **Yogasanas and Sadhana** may prove more and more useful to the students of Yoga, it has been revised again and again. We hope that those who practise Yoga will derive full advantage from this book and extend the benefit to other. We also hope that the readers will pardon the deficiencies in this book the offer their valuable suggestions so that the future editions may be improved.

Dholan Dass Aggarwal
2073, Katra Tambako
Khari Baoli, Delhi-6

Dr. Satya Pal
J-11, Sector-12
Noida-201 301 UP

Yoga is a Scientific Way to Health

Yoga is the art of living and Yogasana is a scientific procedure. This is the only exercise which affects the inmost parts of the body. The health of our body and mind depends on the soundness of the health of our internal organs—the heart, lungs, digestive system, glands, mind, the nervous system, etc. If the organs inside the body are active and the body has adequate resistance power, medicine also acts. Otherwise, the medicine leaves behind toxic effects and gives rise to many new diseases and side effects.

Yoga and other Yogic practices awaken the inner strength of the body. While performing Yogic exercise, we turn and twist the body, stretch it tightly and then release it. Through this process, our blood veins and cleaned up and the heart is helped in pumping purified blood into the body and returning impure blood to the heart. The heart has to function constantly. In a span of 24 hours it pumps 8,000 litres of blood in the body and returns the same amount of impure blood to the heart and transmits it to the lungs for purification. The blood then returns to the heart. This routine process goes on until we are alive.

We tire after the day's work, have to take rest thereafter and sleep at night for 6 to 8 hours, but the heart and the lungs continue working even then. Nor are they subordinate to us. We cannot command them to rest. Even so, the heart also needs rest, and there is only one way of giving it rest and that is the heart and veins should be kept clean so that they might easily circulate purified blood through the whole body and pass the impure blood to the lungs for purification. The heart should not have to carry this job by making hard knocks. The organs receive pure blood are strong, active and disease-free. But today heart diseases are very common. The heart has to function by pressing and pushing and consequently neither pure blood

8

reaches all the parts of the body, not is the toxin ejected from the body. As a result the patient's condition deteriorates and he becomes tense.

Yogasana and Pranayama purify the blood vessels, open up the lungs and the muscles becomes elastic. This boosts their contracting and expanding power. They can absorb more oxygen. They burn up the toxins of the body and eject them in the form of carbon dioxide.

There are 16 to 18 crore pores in lungs, giving it properties like a sponge, where blood is soaked and stored for a while, before cleaning by Oxygen inhaled through respiratory system. If we inhale more oxygen it can reach remotest pores in lungs, ensuring maximum quality of purified blood, resulting in increased flow of blood stream, pumped by heart, to all parts of the body. With the help of various yogic postures we expel toxins from the body and bring control over the body. Daily routine of yogic postures we activate four toxin expelling mechanism viz Nose, Skin, Urinary & Excreta tract, are activated. Thus toxins do not accumulate in the body giving feeling of well being and mental relaxation.

Yogic exercises activate digestive system, and produce sufficient quantity of digestive juices improving appetite, better functioning of colon gland, completely digesting the food, resulting in vigor and improving immune system.

Yogic exercises are probably the only system which aim to improve flexibility of spine. The body is bent in all four directions as well as given twisting movements to achieve the flexibility of the opine as well as activating energy centres of the body. The spine has 26 vertebrae and is divided in three regiments. Uppermost portion is attached to neck region and is called Cervical Region, having 7 vertebrae central portion, called Dorsal Region, behind ribs, has 12 vertebrae lower portion with 7 vertebrae is called Lumber Region.

The cervical region is so formed that we can move the neck, right, left, up, down and tilt it to right & left, vertebrae of spine have hole on either side and in middle. They are fitted into each other to form the column. Between two vertebrae there is cushioning shocker to absorb shocks and compressing loads, protecting other parts of the body. Spinal cord or Sushumna Nadi passes through the length of the spine.

Spinal cord and its activation are mentioned in yoga. Along the spinal cord centre of energy-CHAKRAS-are imagined to be located. By activating these centres a person is relaxed and becomes tension-free.

It is longitudinal cord of nerves extending from the brain along the back in the Spain canal. The spinal canal lodges the spinal cord and is formed by the arches on the dorsal side of the vertebrae. The spinal cord is protected by the axial skeleton in the trunk and tail of the vertebrate consisting of an articulated series of vertebrae. The spine constitutes the control axis or the chief support of the body. Thirty-one pairs of nerves issue from the spinal cord. The left side is call 'ida' (ईडा नाड़ी) never centres and the right the 'Pingla' nerves centres (पिंगला नाड़ी मंडल). It is directly connected to the nasal veins of 'Ida' and'Pingla' (Chandra Nadi and Surya Nadi—चन्द्र नाड़ी और सूर्य नाड़ी—respectively).

The brain is connected with the spinal cord through the foramen magnum. It is the portion of the vertebrate central nervous system which constitutes the organ of thought and neural coordination like a telephone wire network. The brain includes all the higher nerve centres. It receives stimuli from the sense organs and interprets and correlates them to formulate the major impulses. Through this process we experience, for example, heat, cold etc. Indeed the brain activates the whole body by means of these nerve centres. Yogasanas keep our brain and the whole nervous system active and functional. These activities are carried out only in slow motion. During their performance we stretch and relax our physical structure fully. This frees the nerves from stress and strain and improves their functioning. Pranayama also makes the nerves calm and active, the mind steady and increases self-confidence and is the only approach to self discovery.

When the physical structure is healthy the mind is serene, which, in turn, activates the inner powers. The man becomes steady and concentrated. This boosts our working capacity and success follows our efforts. The tendency to shy away from difficult situations vanishes. Rather, we acquire the power of facing up to them. Thinking becomes positive and constructive and our actions have the right direction. Well-being, success and good fortunes thus acquired will evoke joy and bliss which is the other name for 'God'. The soul becomes divine. This is what Yoga is all about. No matter what our field of activity is, by the constant practice of Yoga we remain in the state of Yoga. All that is needed is to perform all kinds of activities connected with it with faith and trust and reverence. This is what accomplishment is—the accomplishment of Yoga.

Treatment through Asanas

Disease	Yogasanas, Mudras and Pranayama
1. **Acidity indigestion, gas**	Paschimottana, Vajra, Pawanamukta, Hala, Mayura, Uddiyan ,Bandha, Kapalbhati, Nauli.
2. **Asthma**	Matsya, Suptavajra, Bhujanga, Shalabha, Ushtra, Kona, Ujjayee, Sahaja Nadi Shodhana, Neti, Kunjal.
3. **Blood Pressure (High)**	Suptavajra, Siddha, Padma, Hala, Matsya, Shithila, Paschimottana, Nadi Shodhana (without Kumbhaka), Dhyana, Ujjayee, Shava, Bhramari.
4. **Blood Pressure (Low)**	Sarvanga, Hala, Paschimottana, Vajra, Padma, Siddha, Sahaja Nadi Shodhana, Shava, Kapalbhati.
5. **Chronic Constipation**	Makara, Uttanpada, Sarvanga, Kapalbhati, Sahaja Nadi Shodhana, Enema.
6. **Colds**	Sahaja Nadi Shodhana, Shirsha, Uddiyana Bandha, Jala Neti, Bhastrika.
7. **Diabetes**	Hala, Paschimottana, Chakra, Ardhamatsyendra, Matsyendra, Sarvanga, Shirsha, Janusira, Suptavajra, Mayura, Uddiyana Bandha, Nadi Shodhana, Antrik Kumbhaka.
8. **Ear, Nose, Throat Disease**	Jala Neti, Sutra Neti, Matsya, Suptavajra, Sarvanga, Singha,

12

Ujjayee, Jallandhara Bandha, Sheetli, Sheetkari, Neti.

9. Headache — Paschimottana, Hala, Sarvanga, Shava, Sahaja Nadi Shodhana.

10. Hernia (Navel) — Suptavajra, Matsya, Hastapadottana, Paschimottana, Sarvanga, Uddiyana Bandha, Kapalbhati.

11. Heart Diseases — Ujjayee, Sahaja Nadi Shodhana (without Kumbhaka), Dhyana, Shava.

12. Kidney Troubles — Shalabha, Dhanura, Janusira, Mayura, Yogmudra, Matsya, Ardhamatsyendra, Nauli, Uddiyana, Moola, Kapalbhati, Nadi Shodhana, Kunjal.

13. Lung Troubles — Matsya, Suptavajra, Sarvanga, Paschimottana, Ujjayee, Sheetli, Sheetkari, (without Kumbhaka), Neti.

14. Liver Troubles — Ushtra, Chakra, Hala, Garbha, Mayura, Sarvanga, Yogamudra, Nauli, Uddiyana Bandha, Nadi Shodhana, Kunjal.

15. Menstruation — Dhanura, Yogamudra, Matsya, Suptavajra, Paschimottana, Garbha, Uddiyana, Kapalbhati, Sahaja Nadi Shodhana.

16. Obesity — Paschimottana, Ardhamatsyendra, Sarvanga, Mayura, Dhanura, Suptavajra, Uddiyana Bandha, Bahya Kumbhaka, Nauli, Kapalbhati.

17. Piles — Sarvanga, Matsya, Shalabha, Dhanura, Makra, Moola Bandha, Ujjayee, Nadi Shodhana, Enema.

18. Semen Troubles	Paschimottana, Janusira, Dhanura, Shirsha, Ardhamatsyendra, Singha, Moola Bandha, Uddiyan Bandha, Nadi Shodhana, Antrik Kumbhaka, Siddha, Badhpadma, Goraksha, Dhyana.
19. Tuberculosis	Sarvanga, Yogamudra, Paschimottana, Nadi Shodhana.
20. Fatness	Paschimottana, Ardhamatsyendra, Sarvanga, Mayura, Dhanura, Suptavajra, Uddiyan Bandha, Bahya Kumbhaka, Nauli, Kapalbhati.

1. The Structure of Human Body

The yoga is a complete subject giving insight to the participant and answer to a major question "Who Am I?" is found by the adept by faith & self discipline. The answer to this question is in eternity and beyond physical structure. It is therefore necessary to know the physical strucure of the body. The structure of human body is so perfect that one may call it a miracle. All its organs work automatically and the body as a whole can remain healthy without any external aids, like medicines etc. What is required is to follow certain laws of nature and the rest would be taken care of by the body itself.

Just as a house is built with several types of big and small bricks, cement, lime and mud, in the same way the body of living beings is made up of certain 'building blocks'. The only difference between the two is that while the blocks used in the body have life, those used in the building of a house are lifeless. These living units are called *cells*. These cells have many shapes and sizes—some are big, others are small, some flat, while others are round. But they cannot be seen with the naked eye.

To take another analogy, the body can be compared to a big state. As the functions of a state are divided into several departments and those departments are responsible for the functions assigned to them, similarly, there are several departments in a human body. Several body organs combine to make one such department. There is perfect co-ordination between one department and another, as well as within the organs of one department. If there is any disorder in this cooperative functioning, the body is unable to perform its functions properly. Yogasanas are practised to keep this functioning in perfect order.

The following are the 'main departments' or centres of the body:

15

1. *Bones centre:* Bones
2. *Joints centre:* Joints of bones
3. *Muscles centre:* Muscles
4. *Blood and blood circulation centre:* Its organs help in the circulation of blood in the whole body, including veins and arteries.
5. *Respiratory centre:* Those organs which help us in breathing, such as nostrils, lungs, etc.
6. *Feeding centre:* Mouth, teeth, liver, intestines etc.
7. *Urine carrying centre:* The organs where the urine is separated as well as the organs which carry urine such as kidneys, urinary bladder etc.
8. *Nerve centre:* This consists of brain, sensory nerves and other organs, which help the brain to govern the body.
9. *Special sense organs:* Eyes, ears, skin, nose and tongue.
10. *Procreative organs:* Those organs which help in procreation such as penis, uterus, ovary, etc.

In addition to these, there are several types of glands which carry on their respective jobs in the human body.

Human body is made up of five elements: air, water, fire, earth and ether. These five elements are present in our body in the form of five sense organs. Ether has the characteristic of sound, which we hear with our ears. The characteristic of air is touch, which we feel with our skin. The characteristic of fire is light, which we feel with our eyes. The characteristic of water is taste which we feel with our tongue. And similarly, the characteristic of earth is smell, which we experience through our nose.

Man has five service organs: mouth, feet, hands, procreative organs and rectum.

Five service organs, five sense organs, the various centres or departments of the body and the glands—in all these 24 elements regulate the functioning of our body. But they are all controlled by the mind which is in turn controlled by the intellect. As the Hindu philosophy puts it, man's ego controls his intellect and the master of ego is the soul.

Yogasanas influence the spinal cord, the muscles, the blood circulation centre, the nerve centre and the digestive organs. All these are closely connected with the heart, lungs, and the brain. It is, therefore, necessary to broadly explain the structure and functioning of these organs.

Vertebral Column (Spine)

Vertebral column runs from neck to waist through the backbone. It has 26 parts which are connected with each other like a chain. These parts are called vertebrae. If the vertebral column had only one bone, the neck and the waist could not have separate movements as they have now. Our health is closely linked with the health of our vertebral column. Our health and youth depend on how flexible our vertebral column is and how clean the 26 vertebrae are, so that they have no obstruction in their free movements. Out of the total 26 vertebrae, 7 are in the neck, 12 in the back and 5 in the waist. The remaining 2 are below the waist near the anus.

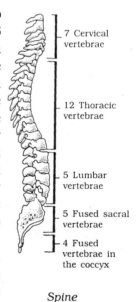

7 Cervical vertebrae

12 Thoracic vertebrae

5 Lumbar vertebrae

5 Fused sacral vertebrae

4 Fused vertebrae in the coccyx

Spine

Muscles

The body skeleton has some soft organs which are connected with the bones by fibrous tissues. They also help in the proper functioning of the body like several other glands. To provide a cover for the bones and to give protection to the glands, we have muscles which also make the body more shapely. These muscles are covered by fat and the fat is subsequently covered by the skin which is visible from outside.

The unique characteristic of the muscles is that they can contract and expand, and again come back to their original positions. These movements of the muscles are called contraction and expansion.

Movements

There are two types of movement in our body. First, there are movements that can be controlled by us at will such as walking, sleeping, raising hand, chewing food, etc. These are called 'voluntary movements'. The second type of our body movements are those which are not under our control. We cannot stop them at will, and similarly cannot put them into action when they are at rest. Our heart keeps on beating without any effort on our part and we cannot stop it. Our intestines also have movements, due to which our food keeps on sliding down. Similarly, the pupils of our eyes contract in excess light and expand in darkness. Such movements cannot be controlled at will and are therefore called 'involuntary movements.'

Blood Circulation Centre and Lungs

In shape man's heart resembles his closed fist. It is located inside the chest under the left nipple. It can be felt by putting a hand on the chest or when the heart-beats become fast and more pronounced after running or in a state of great excitement.

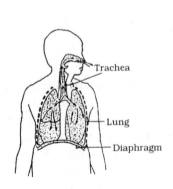

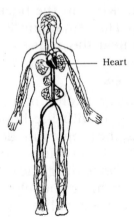

Heart, Arteries and Veins

18

There are arteries and veins for the distribution of blood from the heart to the entire body and again to carry back impure blood to the heart. These are spread in all parts of our body. Some of these are even thinner than hair. Those which carry the pure blood to the entire body are called arteries, and those which bring back the impure blood to the heart are called veins.

To the right of the heart is the right lung and to the left is the left lung. The heart is enclosed within a sac of muscles and tissues.

The heart is a muscular organ. It is divided into two distinct halves by a muscular wall called the septum. Each side of the heart is divided into two chambers, one above the other. These chambers are connected with thin valves, which open downwards only. The blood can flow from the upper chamber to the lower chamber, but it cannot go from the lower chamber to the upper chamber. In this way, there are four such chambers in the heart.

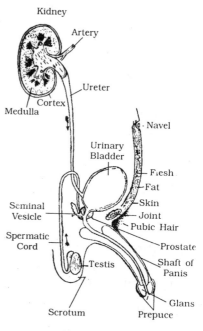

Urinary Track

The heart is always at work—expanding and contracting. Its contraction and expansion are repeated in a rhythmic cycle. A short period of rest follows each contraction.

Lungs are those organs which purify the blood. After it is purified in the lungs, the blood comes back to the left receiving chamber by four veins. When this chamber gets filled, it begins to contract and the blood flows from it to the downward left chamber. The valve of the lower chamber then begins to close. When this chamber contracts, the valve closes completely, so that the blood cannot go back again to the upper chamber. After the contraction of the chamber, the blood goes to the arteries and many branches of these arteries carry it to all parts of the body.

Heart, Arteries and Veins

After pumping out the blood, the heart chambers begin to expand and soon achieve full expansion. This contraction and the closure of the valves produce distinct rhythmic sounds which are called heart-beats. The heart of the normal human adult makes 70 to 75 heart-beats in a minute. In children, the heart-beat is faster. However, in the old age it becomes slow. In one stroke, the heart pumps 60 to 80 grams of blood. It sends six kilograms of blood to the body every minute. This process continues as long as the man lives.

Organs That Purify Blood

Lungs, kidneys, skin, liver, spleen amd many other glands help in the process of the purification of blood. Lungs throw out three types of wastes from the body: (i) Carbon dioxide, (ii) impurities in gas form and (iii) water vapour. They take in only one thing and that is oxygen.

Breathing

The process of inhaling air by the lungs through the nose and then exhaling it out is called breathing. One should always breathe through nose and not through the mouth. Unlike the mouth nostrils have the arrangement of filtering and warming the air before it goes to the lungs. This prevents many impurities from entering the lungs.

Generally, a normal human being breathes 16 to 20 times per minute. In the childhood, the number of breaths in a minute is greater. Breathing rate increases when we undertake physical work like running, jumping and playing. The rate of breathing is greater during the day time than at night—and so it is while standing than lying down.

Brain and The Nervous System

Our brain is enclosed in our skull. The nervous system originates here and spreads to all parts of the body. The organs which help us to think are located in the brain. It is through them that we experience the feelings of joy and sorrow as well as the sensations of light, darkness, heat and coldness. These organs exercise control on the other organs of the body. The nervous system can be compared to the monarch placed in the capital of the body. If we operate upon the skull, the brain can be seen inside it. The shape of the brain is like the kernel of a walnut.

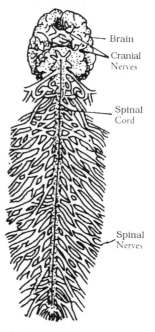

The brain controls the operations of the body through the neurons (nerve fibres). These fibres resemble a strong string, which is not easily broken by pulling and when cut appears solid from inside.

Brain and Nervous System

Functions of the Sensory Nerves

Sensory nerves operate like electric wires. Just as electric wires carry messages from one place to another, these live nerves also carry messages from one place of the body to another. The brain rules the body like a king, and the nerves are its messengers or agents. The orders of the brain reach other organs through these sensory nerves.

The brain can be divided into two main parts: large and small. The large part has several smaller parts which play different roles in different parts of the body. If one part is concerned with the movements of the body, the

21

others give the feeling of pain, heat, coldness etc. Some parts have their relationship with the power of thinking and reasoning, some with seeing, smelling and tasting. Though separate, these parts are connected with each other through nerves.

There are two centres of the 'larger' brain on right and left. The right centre controls the left part of the body while the left controls the right part. These centres are responsible for their territories like the officers in charge of departments or like the district officers of a district in a State. If the need arises, they work in cooperation with one another.

Whenever there is any movement in our body, some muscles contract and others expand. Both these things are necessary for each and every movement of the body. When we bend our elbow, the front muscles become loose. If the contracting muscles do not contract and the expanding muscles do not expand, it would not be possible for us to bend our elbow. The same is true of the movements like walking, sitting, standing and chewing.

Whereas some muscles are ordered by the brain through the sensory nerves to contract, the others are ordered to stop contraction. When both these orders are conveyed and obeyed properly, only then can we move our limbs. The 'small' brain is responsible for the proper conduct of all these movements.

Spinal Cord (सुषुम्ना नाड़ी)

Before Digestive System 'सुषुम्ना' or spinal cord is mentioned alongwith 'कुंडलिनी'. Activation of these two centres is mentioned in scriptures. It is also believed that 'CHAKRAS' or nerve-centres are also located along the spinal cord. By activating these CHAKRAS a man can be in state of relaxed, disease free and peaceful existence. Spinal cord begins from below the skull along the spine and goes up to last but one vertebrae. Its shape is like a twisted rope. On either side of the cord there are

22

31 pairs of nerve-groups. The nerves located on left side are called ईड़ा नाड़ी मंडल and the one on right side is named पिंगला नाड़ी मंडल. They are linked directly with nasal nerves called चन्द्र (moon) and सूर्य (sun).

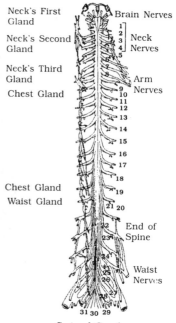

Spinal Cord

Body is controlled by mind with the help of spinal cord and nervous system starting along the length of this cord. The nervous system works like network of comm-unication line to transmit information and pass instructions to and from mind in reflex action. The formation of our body is complete with in-built systems of self-curing and cleaning. Medicines have no role in these functions. All the systems can be made to function efficiently resulting in good health by regularly following yogic system of postures & cleaning process.

Postures or Asanas improve flexibility of the spine, improve functioning of nerves and complete body starts becoming balanced and free of ailments, Pranayam and meditation affect the CHAKRAS. All the five Senses—Hearing, Touch, Taste, Sight and Smell—improve, mind is controlled and efficiency in workplace improves. Self confidence improves and one can face difficulties to solve the problems in daily life.

Functions of the Digestive Organs

For the proper functioning of the body and for giving it the required energy, we need food. Food is first chewed by the teeth in the mouth, where saliva gets mixed with it. This saliva is a digestive juice and helps in the digestion of food. It also softens and moistens the food so that it can easily go down our throat into the food canal which is

23

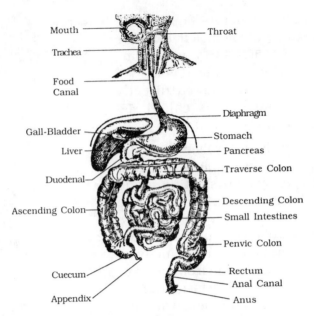

Digestive System

connected to our stomach. In the canal it gets mixed with another juice. The food then passes into the stomach where it undergoes many chemical changes. In the stomach, the food is churned the same way as the curd is churned for making butter.

The stomach is connected to the small intestine. At the joint of these two is a covering or valve. When food is churned completely, this valve opens automatically and the food is transferred to the small intestine. This process goes on in the stomach for three to five hours. If the food is light, the stomach soon becomes empty. But if the food is heavy or full of chillies and spices or fried, it takes longer time to be digested. In the intestines it gets mixed with several other juices, which help in its digestion. The small intestine takes out the digested food elements and absorbs them in its walls. It then pushes the food through the motion of contraction and expansion. The small intestine is about 7 metres long. The food juices absorbed by the intestines go to the liver and the waste material passes through the length of the small intestine and goes over to the large intestine. This process goes on in the small intestine for five to seven hours.

The small intestine absorbs almost the entire food juice. Whatever is left is taken by the large intestine and the waste product is passed on to the exterior, called the rectum. This process also takes about six to seven hours. This way, our body takes about 14 to 18 hours to completely digest a food item.

The food juice extracted from the food by this process then goes to liver, which makes blood from it and sends the blood to the heart. The other dirty liquid is sent to the kidneys. The kidneys purify it and send the uric acid to the bladder, from where it comes out in the form of urine.

In this way nature has made our body a well-organised unit without leaving any flaw in it. It is not that the foot is pricked with a thorn and the hands do not try to take it out or the eyes refuse to find the exact place of the prick. When the foot gets a thorn, the other parts help it to remove it. External attacks on our body are faced by the organs collectively: the brain thinks and commands, the eyes see, the hands exert their force and take the thorn out. In the same way, if the body is attacked by a disease, all the concerned organs try their best to throw it out and to free the body from it. If we do not prevent the organs to do so by our wrong food or by taking medicines, the organs do their best to throw out the disease. *Yogasanas* are very essential for the proper functioning of our organs, and for the accumulation of protective energy in the organs, so that the body continues to function in normal and healthy way.

Glands and Their Functions

1. Pineal Gland: This gland is located in the brain. Its proper functioning helps to improve thinking power and intelligence and the whole body gets tenacity and balance. This gland is influenced by *Sarvangasana* and *Shirshasana*.

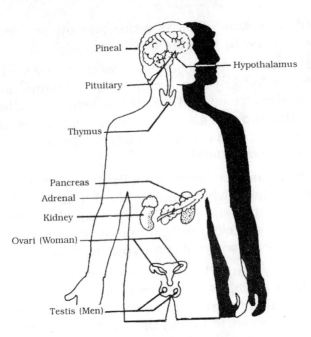

Pineal — Hypothalamus
Pituitary
Thymus
Pancreas
Adrenal
Kidney
Ovari (Woman)
Testis (Men)

Glands

2. Pituitary Gland: This gland is located at the place in the brain where the sensory nerves originate. This gland helps in the balanced growth of all the organs. Its proper functioning prevents obesity and general deficiencies of the body. As a result, procreative organs develop properly, the appetite increases, the old age does not come so soon and generally diseases do not grip the body. *Shirshasana* strengthens it.

3. Thyroid Gland: It helps keep the balance of all the chemical activities in the body, increases the secretion of digestive juices, helps a person gain height and adds to the power of thinking. It is located inside the neck. It helps to increase appetite and to develop the organs of procreation and manliness. It is influenced by *Sarvangasana, Halasana, Bhujangasana* and *Matsyasana.*

4. Liver: This gland is located on the right side under the ribs in the abdomen. It secretes a brownish green fluid, called bile and distributes the food in the body in a proper way. It helps to prevent abdominal ailments; keeps a balance in the proportions of *vaat* (wind) *pitt* (bile) *kaph* (phlegm); provides heat to the entire body, and helps to remove the impurities from the body. *Suryanamaskar, Yogamudra, Paschimottanasana* and *Ardhamatsyendrasana* help it to function more effectively.

5. Spleen: This is located in the abdomen near the stomach and is influenced by all the asanas involving sitting posture. It helps in the digestion of food, purifies the blood and produces white corpuscles.

6. Pancreas: It is also located in the abdomen near the stomach. It secretes digestive juices. It helps in sending the food elements to all parts of the body, overcomes the sugar deficiency, provides sugar for energy, converts proteins and fats into sugar and controls diabetes. It also increases appetite and ensures general activity and strength of the body. It is influenced by *Uddiyan Bandh, Nauli Kriya* and *Ardhamatsyendrasana.*

7. Adrenal Gland: It is located in the abdomen on the left side under the navel. Its functions include increasing of blood circulation and digestive juices and the contraction of the arteries. It helps to prevent constipation and other stomach ailments. The body becomes light and active by its proper functioning. This gland is particularly influenced by *Mayurasana.*

8. Kidneys: These are two in number and are located on both sides of the vertebral column in the stomach. They purify the blood and produce urine, and thus help in the removal of uric acid from the body. They are specially influenced by *Bhujangasana, Dhanurasana* and *Shalabhasana.*

9. Testicles: These are located below the penis in the shape of two balls. Secretion of male seminal fluid, development of procreative organs, separation of fats and generation of male voice in males are some of their major functions. Their proper functioning brings about a balance, sobriety, energy and peace. *Gorakshasana, Siddhasana* and *Padmasana* help them in their functioning.

Shanti Patha

ओ३म् द्यौ शान्तिरन्तरिक्ष ॐ शान्ति पृथिवी शान्तिराप:
शान्तिरोषधय: शान्ति। वनस्पतय: शान्ति विश्वेदेवा:
शान्तिर्ब्रह्म शान्ति: सर्व ॐ शान्ति: शान्तिरेव
शान्ति सामा शान्तिरेधि ओ३म् शान्ति: शान्ति: शान्ति:।

Meaning

May there be peace in the heaven, in the space, on the earth and in the seas! May there be peace in the herbs, in the entire vegetation and in the gods of the world! Brahma may rest in peace and all may bathe in the ocean of peace! May there be peace within me and peace everywhere!

2. Six Types of Yogic Purification Practices

here are no better means than the yogic system of purification to keep the body clean, healthy and beautiful. Our body has three basic properties: *vaat*, *pitt* and *kaph*. If these three are present in the body in a balanced form, the body remains pure and disease-free. Six-fold yogic purification practices help to maintain them in a balanced form. If this balance is disturbed, the body becomes susceptible to several kinds of diseases. Those who do these practices regularly will generally have no ailments. But if any ailment is contracted by the body, the same can be removed by these practices. Our present-day habit of consuming undesirable food and leading fast life are the cause of several body disorders through the accumulation of impurities in the body. To remove these diseases the six-fold yogic purification practices are prescribed so that the body may function properly in its natural way. The six types of yogic purification practices are: *Neti, Dhauti, Nauli, Basti, Kapalbhati* and *Trataka*.

NETI KRIYA

Neti is of several types, but major ones are: *Sutra Neti* and *Jal Neti*.

Sutra Neti

The cotton thread for *Sutra Neti* can be obtained from any *yogashrama*. This is to be done in the morning after brushing the teeth.

Sit down on your feet and raise your neck a little. Wet the cotton thread and put the waxed-end in that nostril through which the breath is passing. When it reaches the throat, catch it with your third and fourth fingers and bring it out through your mouth. Repeat this process with the

29

second nostril also. After practising this for a few days, rub it giving a few jerks by holding the two edges of the thread from the nostril and the mouth. Take it out through your mouth. Take care to wash the thread properly after use, so that no impurity remains. If *Sutra Neti* is not available, buy cathadore (rubber tube) of number 4 or 5 from the office of the Yoga Sansthan. Infact, rubber tube is more in vogue these days.

कपाल शोधिनि चैव दिव्यदृष्टि प्रदायिनी।
यत्रध्वजातरोगौधं नितिराशु निहंति च॥ (हठयोग प्रदीपिका 30)

That is, *Neti* purifies and cleans the skull (fore-head) and confers heavenly insight on the practiser. It drives away the diseases that appear on the joints of chest and eyes.

Advantages: *Neti* cleans the skull, improves eyesight, protects the body from the diseases of ear, nose and throat; from cold, headache and deafness of the ear; and from undesirable growth of the nasal bone.

If the rubbing of the thread inside the nose causes any burning sensation or if blood oozes out of the nose, put a few drops of ghee in both the nostrils. Usually one should also put a few drops of ghee in the nostrils before going to bed at night, and inhale them in. This practice is very useful.

Sutra Neti

Jal Neti

A bowl or pot or *lota* with a pipe-like opening is used for this kriya (please see picture). Dissolve some salt in lukewarm water and fill the pot with this water. Raise the nostril that is active at the time of breathing towards one side and fit the pipe's mouth into it. Open the mouth and start breathing through it. Now tilt the pot gradually in such a manner that the water goes inside the nostril. The water should come out through the second nostril as it is at a lower level. Now repeat this process by putting the pipe in the second nostril.

Caution: When doing it, never use your nose for breathing.

Jal Neti

Bhastrika Pranayama is a must atter *Jal Neti*. To do this bow a little forward and move the neck right, and left; up and down, and then do *Bhastrika*, so that the nose gets completely clean and dry. No trace of water should be allowed to remain inside the nostrils.

After you have mastered this technique completely, you can practise drinking water or milk through the nose. Drinking of milk or water through the nose has specific advantages. It cures all brain ailments and sharpens the intellect. The ailments of eyes, ears, nose, throat are cured and sleeplessness removed. It also improves the eye sight.

Dhauti Kriya

Dhauti is the process of gradually swallowing a muslin cloth (7 meters x 8 cm) soaked in salt water, and then of taking it out slowly.

31

This bandage-shaped cloth must be washed thoroughly with hot water before the use. To begin with, keep the bandage in a cup full of dilute saline solution. Take one end of the bandage, and put it in your mouth. Then chew it slowly like animals and insert it in your stomach. Be careful to do this gradually on the first day. Swallow only one metre cloth and then go, on increasing the length.

Dhauti Kriya

After inserting the cloth in your stomach, pull it out by a slow process. If there is any obstruction, chew a little more and then bring it out. However, if there is a difficulty in swallowing the cloth in the beginning, soak the cloth in water mixed with milk or honey. If the pull out process is obstructed due to some reasons, drink salted water and vomit, and then take the cloth out. After use, the dhauti cloth should be washed with soap so that impurities sticking on it are removed.

By this process, the phlegm of the stomach comes out. Diseases like cough, asthma, headache, fever, leprosy as well as the diseases of breathing and liver are cured by this kriya. It gives perfect health to a person and makes him strong. It increases appetite and removes gas and other stomach troubles.

Kunjal Kriya

Those who are not able to perform *Dhauti* can practise *Kunjal* to clean their stomach. This kriya consists of drinking salted lukewarm water and then vomiting it out. Just as an elephant drinks water with his trunk and then throws it out, similarly this process is also practised. It is therefore, also sometimes called *Gaj Karni*, meaning 'elephantal process'.

Kunjal should be done on the empty stomach. It can also be done in case of stomach upset and food poisoning so that poisonous food is thrown out. This is very useful for a person having bile (*pitt*) characteristics.

Technique: Sit in *Utkatasana*, the posture of sitting on one's feet. Drink lukewarm water about two or two-and-a-half litres in a quick succession. Stand up and bend a little forward. Keep your hands on your thighs. Take two of your fingers inside your mouth and vomit, bending forward. Repeat it two or three times until the entire water comes out. After sufficient practice, it would be no longer necessary to take the fingers into the mouth.. Have breakfast of milk some time after this.

Advantages: It helps in curing the diseases like dyspepsia, jaundice, indigestion, food poisoning, worms and also the diseases of the skin and blood. The stomach is cleaned and appetite increases.

Caution: Heart patients, and those having weak intestines as well as those suffering from sprue should not practise this.

Healthy persons should normally practise this once a week.

Basti Kriya

This is the process of sucking the water into the large intestine through the rectum, and then throwing it out. This can be done in two ways.

(i) Stand in navel-deep water or sit in *Utkatasana* in knee-deep water. Fit a rubber tube or a tube made of thin bamboo into your rectum and suck the water in your large instestine while doing *Uddiyan Bandh*.

Now shake your belly and throw the water out. These days enema has become more common than this.

(ii) **_Through Enema:_** Put some warm water in an enema pot. A little salt or lemon juice can also be mixed in it. Keep the pot on a raised platform. First take out some water through the nozzle so that the air inside the tube is exhausted. Grease the nozzle with a little oil, lie down on your left side and put the nozzle (one-and-a-half inch) inside the rectum. Open the water and exercise deep breathing. The water will go into the large intestine. Half litre water can be sucked in the intestine. Shake your belly, change sides and go to latrine after staying in this position for 10 to 15 minutes. Take light breakfast some time after this.

Caution: Enema should always be done on an empty stomach.

Advantages: It cleans the stomach and helps in the cure of stomach ailments. The large intestine is washed and cleaned and it thus becomes more strong. The adverse effects of all the three imbalances due to _vaat, pitt_ and _kaph_ are removed. It increases appetite, gives mental peace and makes the body light and active.

A healthy person should take enema twice a month.

Nauli Kriya

Place your hands on your knees and stand on your feet, keeping them about one foot apart. For the first few days, exhale your breath and do _Kumbhaka_ while practising _Uddiyan Bandh_ in this position. After this, put a little weight of your body on your hands and leave the belly in a loose position while stretching it a little towards your chest. Then try to make a tube sort of shape in the middle of your stomach (see picture). After a few days' practice, you will be able to perform this without any difficulty, provided you take light meals and keep your stomach clean.

While the *Nauli* has been formed in the middle of your stomach, press with your right hand. You will see that the *Nauli* will move towards the left of your stomach. Similarly, if the left hand is pressed, the *Nauli* will move towards right. In this way, *Nauli* can be moved from left to right and from right to left. When you have had sufficient practice, move the *Nauli* right and left with speed.

Nauli Kriya

Note: All *kriyas* of *Nauli* are to be performed after exhaling and in *Bahya Kumbhaka*.

Advantages: *Nauli* removes the impurities stuck on the lining of the intestines. It also removes constipation, obesity and dyspepsia. The liver, spleen and other glands are influenced by this practice. *Vaat, pitt* and *kaph* disorders are removed, the stomach remains light and the appetite increases. It makes a man physically and mentally alert and strong.

Caution: Those who suffer from sprue or of swelling of the intestines should not practise *Nauli*.

Kapalbhati Kriya

For detailed description of *Kapalbhati* refer to the chapter on *Pranayama*. This process melts the phlegm in lungs and in the veins carrying phlegm and excretes it through perspiration. By this, the lungs become healthy, strong and free from impurities. This also activates *Sushumna*, which ensures peace of mind.

Caution: Those suffering from heart disease, jaundice, or insomnia should not practise this *Pranayama*.

Trataka Kriya

निरीक्षेन्निश्चलदृश सूक्ष्मलक्ष्यं समाहित:।

अश्रुसंपातपर्यंतं माचार्यैस्त्राटकं स्मृतम्॥ (हठयोग प्रदीपिका 31)

Meaning: *Trataka* is the process of looking at a fixed point with fullest concentration till tears come to one's eyes, so say the *rishis*.

There are many techniques to do *Trataka* and every one of them has different merits. In yoga literature, it is the process of fixing one's full attention and eyes on the idol of one's worship and devotion.

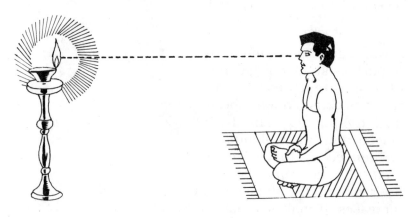

Trataka Kriya

Technique: Sit in *Padmasana*, *Siddhasana* or *Sukhasana* according to your convenience. Hang a paper on a wall at a distance of six or seven feet, making a small black, round patch of the size of a 25 paise coin or with the letter ओ३म् on the paper. Otherwise take a small earthen lamp using mustard oil or pure ghee in it and keep it in front of you. Place the lamp at such a place where its flame does not flicker due to wind. Concentrate on this lamp or black spot without blinking your eyes. When you feel a burning sensation in your eyes or tears start coming, close your eyes slowly. The eyes and attention should be fully fixed on the object, only then is your *Trataka* successful. Gradually increase the duration of the *Trataka*. It can be practised for hours together. You are not required to force your eyes to stretch them to the fullest extent, they have only to be kept open in a natural way. The muscles around the eyes should not be stretched.

Advantages: All ailments of the eyes are cured by this. Laziness and indolence are removed. The mind gets the power of concentration. The *Sadhaka* gets firm determination by this process.

These six-fold yogic practices are the best means of purification of the body. One must learn them from a guru or some knowledgeable person, and should practise according to ones needs. These practices are beneficial both for the body and the mind, and increase their strength and capacity manifold.

Gayatri Mantra

ॐ भूर्भुव: स्व:।
तत्सवितुर्वरेण्यं भर्गो देवस्य धीमहि।
धियो यो न: प्रचोदयात्॥

Meaning

Thou O Supreme Lord, the source of all existence, intelligence and bliss! the Creator of the universe! May we prove worthy of Thy choice and acceptance! May we meet Thy glorious grace! May Thou vouchsafe an unerring guidance to our intellect and may we follow Thy lead into righteousness!

---

3. Ashtang Yoga

The aim of man's life is to be free from worldly sorrows and to get submerged in the Supreme Soul and attain eternal bliss. A man, attached to the tempting delusions of the world, suffers from sorrows and pains. To escape from these sorrows and to attain ultimate merger with the Eternal Being, man has to adopt one of the paths of Karma Yoga, Dhyana Yoga, Jnana Yoga or other yogas.

These are in fact different systems which lead a man to the same goal. The aim of human life is not to be born again and again but to experience eternal bliss or oneness with the Supreme Being. Yoga is second to none for the achievement of this goal.

The word 'Yoga' is derived from the root 'yuj' (युज्) which means union or merger. The merger of soul with God and the experience of oneness with Him is meant by yoga. The state of *Samadhi* can be attained through yoga. This type of effort is possible only through the control over sense organs and through continued practice and detachment. योगश्चितवृत्ति निरोध: 'The withdrawal of sense organs from the worldly objects and their control is yoga'. *Samadhi* is the ultimate stage of this control.

According to the *Bhagvad Gita*, the practice of yoga fixes the mind on God, thereby giving complete peace to the soul. In such a state, a man experiences unalloyed joys: his mind stops wavering and worldly temptations lose all meanings for him. This state of mind is yoga. One who attains this state becomes a yogi. He attains eternal peace of mind. His mind is free from sins and worldly temptations. He then becomes one with God, free from the bondage of *Karmas*.

There are five states of mind according to our scriptures: *Moodha* (मूढ़) *Kshipta* (क्षिप्त), *Nikshipta* (निक्षिप्त), *Ekagra*

38

(एकाग्र) and *Niruddha* (निरुद्ध). The *Moodha* state is the result of attachment, anger, greed and infatuation. Its chief characteristics are sleep, indolence, fear, laziness, helplessness. *Kshipta* state is the ignorance of what is right and wrong, evil and virtuous, attachment and detachment, knowledge and delusion. This state is Rajasic state of mind. *Nikshipta* state is achieved through *Karmayoga* and through the practice of Sattvic virtues. It leads to happiness, forgiveness, devotion, tolerance, mercy and superior consciousness. Once in sattvic state, one achieves the concentration of mind. In this state one gets full realisation of everything, from an atom to the Supreme Being. This is the state of what has been called विवेक ख्याति (*Vivek Khyati*), the knowledge of the right and the wrong. One gets true knowledge of everything as also detachment from sense objects. In this state, the mind attains self-realization and the false knowledge vanishes. This is also called the state of *Nirveej Samadhi*. Through self-realization one sees God in all or One in all.

Yoga has theoretical as well as practical sides but more emphasis is laid on the practical aspects. Every *Sadhaka* perceives truth for himself during the practice of yoga. The reason why there is so much sorrow in the world is that man has befriended nature or *Maya*, but has forgotten his other friend, the Supreme Person. If he is able to establish his relationship with Him, he would achieve the object of his life. But to establish this relationship, he has to take the path of yoga. Body is the means for achieving all virtues. In yoga, the physical aspect is not neglected but along with this, there is continuous march towards salvation.

Our *rishis* and *munis* have mentioned eight-fold process, *Ashtang yoga*, to attain the purification of body, mind and soul as well as to achieve union with the Supreme Being. This includes *Yama* (यम), *Niyama* (नियम), *Asana* (आसन), *Pranayama* (प्राणायाम), *Pratyahara* (प्रत्याहार), *Dharana* (धारणा), *Dhyana* (ध्यान) and *Samadhi* (समाधि).

Yamas

Yamas mean self-restraint. These are five in number:

(a) *Ahimsa* (अहिंसा): Not to cause injury to any living being through thought, words or deeds. In other words, love of the entire creation is *Ahimsa*.

(b) *Satya* (सत्य): *Satya* or truthfulness is saying exactly what one sees with one's own eyes, hears with one's own ears and understands through one's own brain. It means that truthfulness should not only be external, but internal also.

(c) *Asteya* (अस्तेय): Not to steal anything and not to be greedy of others' wealth or possessions.

(d) *Brahmacharya* (ब्रह्मचर्य): To keep one's sense organs, including the organs of procreation, under control and not to be tempted by the lustful enjoyments through thought, words and deeds.

(e) *Aparigraha* (अपरिग्रह): It means non-covetousness. In *Asteya*, one gives up stealing but may accept charity. But in *Aparigraha*, charity is also not accepted. Hoarding of wealth, riches and other materials of enjoyment for selfish ends is *Parigraha*, while the absence of these is *Aparigraha*.

Niyamas

Niyamas are also five:

(a) *Shaucha* (शौच): It implies purity, internal and external. The purity of mind is specially to be emphasised. The body can be kept clean and pure by Sattvic food, six types of yogic purifications etc. Mind's purity is achieved through giving up of attachment, jealousy and other base ideas, so that man's thinking becomes pure and clean.

(b) *Santosha* (सन्तोष): It means contentment. One should be content with whatever is acquired while doing one's duty truthfully or whatever is received through the grace of God.

40

(c) *Tapa* (तप): It means keeping the mind detached and under control and bear pleasure and pain, heat and cold, hunger and thirst with equanimity.

(d) *Swadhyaya* (स्वाध्याय): It is the study of spiritual books to gain real knowledge and spending one's time in the company of good people and sages and exchanging ideas with them.

(e) *Ishwara pranidhana* (ईश्वर प्राणिधान): It is the complete surrender of self to God in words, deeds and thought. It implies worship of God, chanting of His name, hearing about Him and thinking of Him as all pervasive, omni-present and omniscient.

Asanas

The daily asanas are a must for keeping the body fit and pure. These have been prescribed by our *rishis* for the control of our body and mind (स्थिरं सुखमासनम्). The *asana* has been described as sitting in a posture, which is comfortable and which keeps the body straight and firm. To impart a state of effortlessness to the body, to do away with all the effects of over-indulgence of the body in worldly affairs and to provide it necessary rest is the object of asanas.

Regular practice of *asanas* results in the purification of veins and nerves and promotion of general health of the body. The asanas are of two types. Those which are performed for the sake of *Dhyana* (meditation) such as *Padmasana, Siddhasana* and *Swastikasana* fall in the first category. The second type of asanas are meant to gain physical health. They are *Sarvangasana, Bhujangasana, Chakrasana*, etc. They tone up the entire body system and give it strength and vigour. There are several hundred asanas, alluded to by our sages. But in this book, we will describe only those essential ones which are most useful for a man's health.

Pranayama

Detailed discussion on *Pranayama* is available in the chapter on "Pranayama" in the book. Here, we mention it only in brief. Maharishi Patanjali says: श्वासप्रश्वासयो: गतिविच्छेद: प्राणायाम: (यो. सू 2/49). It means that *Pranayama* is controlling the normal breathing cycle. It helps one to get rid of worldly desires and sensual drives and thereby it leads to knowledge. "तत: क्षीयते प्रकाशावरणम्" (योग दर्शन, 2/52) that is, ignorance which covers the knowledge is destroyed. "धारणासु च योग्यता मनस:" (यो. सू. 2/53): that is, mind becomes capable of concentration. Manu has emphasised प्राणायामैर्दहेत दोषान् that is, evils are burnt by *Pranayama*.

Pranayama activates *Sushumna* and influences the entire nervous system thereby developing latent powers of the man. These powers are also called *Siddhis*, through which miracles can be performed.

Pratyahara

The withdrawal of the senses from their respective outside objects and projecting them inwards is *Pratyahara*. The senses are generally turbulent and restless. The practice of *Pratyahara* brings the senses under control, imparts to the body health and capability to enter *Samadhi* (superconscious state).

Through the practice of *Yamas*, *Niyamas*, *Asanas* and *Pranayama*, the body becomes pure and healthy, mind and senses more restrained and at peace. As a result, it is easy for him to achieve concentration. One gets a glimpse of the powers of God and starts merging himself into Him. All these developments and achievements prepare ground for *Pratyahara*.

According to Patanjali, this is how our external senses come in close and direct contact with mind and intellect.

Our external senses obtain knowledge about external objects, pass it on to the subtle senses in the brain and they in turn communicate it to the mind. The mind submits this to the intellect which passes its judgement on whether it is right or wrong. It then makes this knowledge available to the conscious body located in the heart in the form of *Samskaras*. Our conscious body or consciousness keeps on collecting all these *Samskaras*. In this operation, our external senses then have a direct contact with our mind and intellect, but have no access to consciousness. Even in the state of sleep, only our subtle senses have contact with mind and intellect; the external senses remain unaffected and therefore do not show any reaction. As a result the eyes cannot see even if they are open, ears cannot hear, hands do not move, and feet become inactive. Then the consciousness gets busy in self-analysis or attains the *niruddha* state and lies at rest, with the result that mind and intellect are also at peace. When the senses find that their master is at peace, they stop getting their food from the external world. In this way, the senses get detached from their objects of feeding (the senses of knowledge suspending the activity of collecting information and the service organs not performing their normal functions) and the mind and intellect attain complete rest. This state of mind and body is called *Pratyahara*.

Patanjali has included *Pratyahara* in the five external organs of yoga: *Yamas, Niyamas, Asanas, Pranayama* and *Pratyahara. Dharana, Dhyana* and *Samadhi* are its internal organs.

Dharana

Fixing one's mind on an external object, subtle or otherwise, like heart, lotus, nose or one's favourite deity is called *Dharana*. After the practice of *Yamas, Niyamas, Asanas* and *Pranayama*, this becomes rather easy, especially after *Pratyahara. Pratyahara* brings the mind and the senses under control, so once the mind is at peace it can then concentrate successfully on any object.

It has been stated in the "Moksha Parva" of the *Mahabharata* that the concentration performed in a state of delusion does not lead to achieve its goal. As a boat without oars in the sea cannot lead the passengers to the bank, similarly the boat of *Dharana*, without the oars of consciousness, cannot lead us across to the ocean of life. The sadhaka who practises *Dharana* according to the way shown by the *Shastras*, achieves freedom from cycle of death and rebirth, and all his woes disappear. It is easier to dance on the sharp edge of a sword, than to practise *Dharana* with a turbulent and bewildered mind. Those who want to achieve success in *Dharana* should first regulate their food, thoughts, words and deeds. They should daily practise *Dharana* with perfect dedication.

Dhyana

Meditating with constant attention on the object of concentration is *Dhyana*. It is said in the Upanishads that a sin, which is as high and as stupendous as a mountain, can be pierced only through *Dhyana* and not through any other means. It has been stated in *Vivek Churamani* that *Dhyana* purifies the mind of *Rajas* and *Tamas gunas* and lights the mind with *Sattva guna*, just as an alkali purifies gold and makes it bright and sparkling.

Samadhi

Samadhi is the state of superconsciousness and perfect calm. When the mind becomes one with the form of the object of its concentration in *Dhyana*, it leads one to the state of *Samadhi*. It is the climax of *Dhyana*. When *Dhyana* achieves maturity, the mind loses the sense of duality with the object of concentration (*Dhyana*), leading to the state of *Samadhi*. One has to practise *Dhyana* in its fullest form to reach this stage. In *Dhyana* state, the object of *Dhyana*, the self who practises *Dhyana* and *Dhyana* itself appear to be separate and different from each other. But in the state of *Samadhi*, the only thing left is the object of *Dhyana*, because all the three become one in *Samadhi*, the difference between the self and the object completely disappears.

Dharana, Dhyana and Samadhi, these three are collectively called *Sanyama* in the language of *Yoga Shastras*. When one achieves maturity, the *sattvic* feeling of the object of *Dhyana* is the only thing that remains and the intellect is fixed on this only. This helps to unfold the world of knowledge and wisdom to the seeker and he reaches superconscious state. ❏❏

44

4. The Importance of Yogasanas

Yogasanas are the physical practices which tone up the internal organs of the body. The body that is visible from outside is only a skeleton covered by muscle cells which gives it a shape. In the chapter on the structure of the human body, some information about its internal functioning has been provided. Until and unless our internal organs are healthy, we cannot be healthy. We see that the heart works for all the 24 hours and does not take rest even for a single moment. The heart can get rest only when the nerves carrying the blood to and from the heart are clean. Even a small obstruction in them can cause a major disorder. Our lungs should also function properly and take maximum air full of oxygen for purifying the blood. Similarly our stomach, liver and other glands should secrete their full quantity of juices for the proper digestion of food. The intestines should also extract the maximum food elements from the food. The formation of juices, blood, muscles, fats, bones, semen should take place according to the needs of the body. Our nervous system should get strength so that all body movements can be performed in a proper way. The impurities should not get accumulated in the body and we should be able to enhance our muscle power.

Our body tells us everything. For instance, it tells us when it is hungry or thirsty or tired. Accordingly, we eat food, drink water and take rest. When the body does not require food, it vomits it out. It cannot keep any impurity inside it. What is needed is to give proper attention to it, to hear its call so that it remains active all the time.

But we generally do not pay attention to all this. When the impurity in the body takes the shape of a disease, we run for medicines. What does the medicine do? It usually numbs the nerve tissues which give information about the disease and we become satisfied that we have been cured, although the medicine has only suppressed the disease and not cured it.

It is said by medical experts that in the absence of regular exercise, a chalk-like impurity gets accumulated in the muscles and other body parts. It contains chemical substances like lime-phosphate and magnesia. For the human body, this impurity is like poison. As the age of a person increases, the amount of this poison also increases in such proportions that it is able to damage several parts of our body. By the accumulation of this impurity, the veins and arteries contract, the circulation of blood in the brain becomes slower, the memory is affected and doubts, worries, bad temper take hold of us. But, on the other hand, if we exercise regularly, we can get rid of this impurity thereby enhancing our physical and mental health and increasing our-life span.

But with the growing accumulation of this external matter in the body, the body is adversely affected and we feel weak and lazy. Yogasanas keep the body free from these impurities and make it healthy. They also improve the functioning of our intestines so that the stomach ailments like indigestion, gas, constipation, etc. are cured. The regular practice of yogasanas imparts strength to the body, brightness to the face, high spirits to the mind and impetus to the intellect. Yogic practices help control the senses, thereby creating favourable situation for *Dhyana*. *Dhyana* brings about an excellent state of mind which in turn leads to the highest achievement of human life. All the sorrows then disappear and the problems vanish. The mind rests in peace and experiences bliss.

Some people, however, question why we should prefer yogasanas to other exercises such as gymnastics, wrestling and popular games. What is wrong about doing these exercises and what is very special about yogasanas? The following points will answer their queries:

1. Other exercises affect only the muscles outwardly, therefore, the body appears quite strong and healthy. But these exercises do not have as much impact on the internal organs of the body as the yogasanas. Yogasanas are very effective in throwing out all our body wastes and in activating our glands, on the proper functioning of which depends our health and happiness. They give wonderful powers and increase longevity. Moreover, in doing asanas the number of cells that break is small, while the number of new cells that are formed is proportionately very large.

2. Other exercises have very little impact on the mind and sense organs, while the asanas improve mental power and help in controlling the sense organs.

3. Yogasanas improve our resistance power against diseases and do not allow any external matter to accumulate in the body. In this way, they keep the body free from the diseases.

4. For sports and other exercises, we need considerable space and several persons. Asanas on the other hand can be performed in relatively little space and all by oneself. All that we need is a carpet or bed sheet. But we must learn them first from a person who knows the technique well.

5. Yogasanas increase the elasticity of our body and make the body more active and supple. The blood circulation takes place more smoothly and properly and the body becomes capable of more work. We look young in spite of our age. Other exercises, on the other hand, make the muscles stiff and hard. The body becomes stiff and the old age comes sooner.

6. As a drain is cleaned by sweeping and by putting water into it, the different asanas clean the blood-circulation drains of our body in the same way. Clean blood circulates freely in all parts of our body, and helps keep our body free from impurities. This

is possible only by yogasanas and not by other exercises which increase our heartbeat abnormally. They do not have the capacity to clean the blood unlike the asanas.

7. Our lungs are responsible for purifying our blood. By yogasanas and pranayama, we increase the expansion and contraction of our lungs so that they become capable of purifying more and more blood. In other exercises the lungs breathe quickly, but not deeply. The oxygen, therefore, does not reach their innermost parts. These parts therefore keep on accumulating wastes and impurities and after some time show off as diseases.

8. We usually have an unnatural and wrong way of living in the modern times. We also eat unnatural food and thereby spoil our digestive system. The digestive organs cannot function properly due to this unnatural mode of living and eating. Yogasanas are the best means to keep these organs in proper functioning order. No other exercise can be a substitute for the asanas in this respect.

9. Our youth depends upon our spine which controls the entire nervous system and blood circulatory organs. The greater the elasticity in the vertebral column, the greater the vigour and longer the life.

10. Other exercises cause tiredness to the body, while yogasanas make us fresh. In other exercises, the body has to spend a lot of energy, but in yogasanas it is not so, because these have to be done slowly by stretching the body limbs and then relaxing them. These exercises do not cause any violence to the body. They are therefore known as "non-violent exercises".

11. Other exercises have little impact on the character of a person. But yogasanas not only improve body health, they also have a sobering effect on the mind. They build up mental and ethical powers. The mind becomes balanced and peaceful. This in turn brings about equanimity and *sattvic* ideas.

12. There are several glands in our body which keep us healthy and free from diseases if they function properly. Their secretion mix with blood and the man becomes healthy and strong. For example, if thyroid and parathyroid glands which are located in the neck do not secrete their juices in the required quantity, the children's development is halted and even young men start losing their hair prematurely. The practice of yogasana is very effective in activating these glands, so that they secrete their juices in the required quantity.

13. In fact, yogasanas, pranayama and six yogic practices of purification are a panacea for all ills. They have a unique power to throw waste products out of the body. They can therefore be depended upon for physical and mental well-being.

14. Besides having physical, mental and moral effects, yoga system leads a man to spiritualism. No other system has such wide-ranging impact on human body, mind, brain and intellect.

❑❑

5. Yogasanas: Rules and Technique

The main aim of yogic postures is to have supple body, calm mind and experience balanced spiritual existence. It is therefore, suggested that new adept commence the routine slowly from simple postures and then add difficult asanas. It is recommended that a new adept starts with *Surya Namaskar* (Salutation to Sun), *Nao Asana* (Boat Posture), *Kamarchakrasana* (Spinal Twist Posture), *Vajra Asana* (Hardy Pose), *Ushtra Asana* (Camel Pose), *Bhujanga Asana* (Cobra Pose), *Dhanur Asana* (Bow Pose), *Padauttan Asana* (Raised Feet Pose), *Makar Asana* (Aligator Pose) and *Mukta Asana* (Stomach Squeese).

After about a month's practice, introduce, *Paschimottana Asana* (Posterior Stretch Pose), *Yogmudra* (Variation of Lotus Pose), *Ardhamatsyendra Asana* (The Spinal Twist), *Supta Vajra Asana* (Horizontal Hardy Pose), *Shalabh Asana* (Locust Pose), *Halasana* (Plough Pose), *Sarvanga Asana* (Shoulder Stand), *Matsya Asana* (Fish Pose) etc. one by one.

The following rules about yogasanas must be observed to get maximum benefit from them:

1. Yogasanas should be done in the morning after going to the latrine. It is preferable to practise them after bathing, because bathing makes the body light and fresh, thereby increasing its elasticity. This helps in doing the asanas properly. However, asanas can be done in the evening also, if the stomach is empty.

2. The place of asanas must be clean and peaceful. A good smooth lawn or a garden is preferable. Whatever be the space available, preference should always be given to a place which is open from all sides with adequate inlet for fresh air.

3. A *dari* or a blanket should be spread on the ground chosen for asanas. This would protect you from

small stones etc., which may otherwise hurt you. This would also keep your attention undisturbed which otherwise might be disturbed due to the magnetic effect of the earth.

4. Never talk while doing asanas. Your attention should be on your breath and the organ being affected by the asanas. The greater the concentration, the greater the advantage to the body and the mind. Before starting the asanas, bring your body, breath and mind to completely normal and restful state. If necessary, perform a *Shavasana*.

5. Yogasanas are a non-violent activity. No jerks should be given to the body while doing them. Stretch your limbs very slowly to the fullest extent and then relax. Do not start the next asana until your breath has become normal after an asana.

6. Increase your practice of asanas gradually. By constant practice, your body will become more and more elastic day by day. It may take six months or even a year to assume a perfect posture of a particular asana. Patience as well as faith are therefore very essential—without which you may feel disappointed after the first few days only. Remember that all can do asanas without exception, provided one has patience.

7. Asanas should be done with the minimum of clothes on the body depending upon the season. Underwear or *langot* is a must.

8. Practice of yoga is open to all, from children of 10 years to old men of 80-85 years. Men and women are equal in this respect. Asanas are as useful for women as they are for men.

9. The asanas must be learnt from a *guru* or a person who has thorough knowledge of the subject. Their proper technique must also be learnt first. Remember that yoga is a scientific system. It has its relation with the internal organs of the body. Therefore, doing asanas without understanding the

proper technique may sometimes cause harm instead of good.

10. A yoga practitioner is required to pay due attention to his food also. The food should be light, easily digestible, natural as far as possible and *sattvic*. Light food keeps the body light and fresh, giving more working power to the body.

11. People suffering from fever or chronic diseases should not do asanas. Pregnant women are also forbidden to do them. Asanas should be stopped during menstruation period also. Men suffering from common ailments and normally healthy persons only should do asanas. Consult your instructor always before doing them, if you are suffering from some chronic disease.

12. Begin with easier asanas. Do not do all the asanas at the very start. Keep your eyes closed while doing asanas. Do every asana according to your capacity. The duration of each asana should be increased slowly. *Sarvangasana*, for example, can be done for 2 to 10 minutes according to one's capacity.

13. The order of the asanas should be such that upasana or counterpose of a particular asana ccmes after it, e.g., the upasana of *Paschimottanasana* is *Konasana* and that of *Sarvangasana* is *Matsyasana*. The upasanas should invariably be done after the main asanas.

14. You can yourself judge the advantages of asanas. You can as well see if you are doing them properly or not. If your body becomes fresh, free from tiredness, light and active, and if you feel your working power increased, you should conclude that the asanas are having the desired effect on your body. This criterion will also give you the right indication if you are doing all asanas correctly or not. These asanas help you look youthful.

15. At the end of the asanas, you must do *Shavasana* for some time. You will be able to get full advantage

of the asanas only when you give some rest to your body by doing *Shavasana*. This asana in itself is a complete asana. It endows the body with wonderful powers. See *Yognidra* at page 102.

16.   Do asanas and pranayama for one hour and after that you should not eat anything for atleast half an hour. If you take rest or sleep for an hour after doing the asanas, their effect will be more beneficial. This is because by doing the asanas you have put your inner system to work, and by taking rest it will work vigorously to oust the disease and give strength and power to your body and mind. Do not eat anything till half an hour after performing yogasanas.

Sequence of Postures for Common Ailments

Heart & Blood Pressure: A patient should start with *Kamar Chakra Asana, Vajra Asana, Ushtra Asana, Bhujanga Asana, Shalabh Asana* (One foot at a time), *Makar Asana, Pawan Mukta Asana & Matsya Asana.* All the postures should be done slowly making sure to feel the stretch. After every asana one must rest. Next asana should be undertaken only after the breathing is normalised. As the elasticity of the body increases keep adding new asanas. After completing the routine lie down in Shavasana (Corpse Pose) for 5 minutes or rest for an hour or half an hour.

Diabetic: Concentrate on *Nao Asana, Kamar Chakra Asana, Janushir Asana* (Mahamudra), *Paschimottana Asana, Yogmudra, Ardhamatsyendra Asana, Vajra Asana, Supta Vajra Asana, Mayura Asana, Padauttan Asana, Hala Asana, Makar Asana, Pawan Mukta Asana & Sarvanga Asana.* Slowly add rest of the postures to complete the routine.

Pain in Joints: Person should pay greater attention to *Kamar Chakra Asana, Janam Asana, Akaran Dhanur Asana, Yognidra, Goraksha Asana, Vajra Asana, Supta Vajra Asana, Bhujanga Asana, Makar Asana & Pawan Mukta Asana.*

Cervical Spondylitis: The recommended postures are *Tar Asana* (Standing as well as lying down), *Kamar Chakra*

53

Asana, without bending, *Ardhamatsyendra Asana*, *Supta Vajra Asana*, *Ushtra Asana*, *Bhujanga Asana*, *Padauttan Asana*, *Makar Asana* (with knees bent as well as feet spread out), *Pawan Mukta Asana*, *Matsya Asana* and movement of the neck in all directions. For this lie on back with hands on the sides. Take elbow support and raise upper portion of the body and look towards feet chin reaching the collar bone, bend the head back, look right & left and then rotate in clockwise and anticlockwise direction. Repeated practice of *Ushtra Asana* is extremely beneficial in these cases.

Dhavani Yog

Position: Sit in *Padmasana* or *Siddhasana* with hands in *Gyanmudra* position and elbows slightly bent, make sure spine is straight, shoulders level, head extension of spine i.e., erect, eyes closed and face calm.

Procedure: Breath normally for a few moments. Concentrate on breathing. Now inhale deeply and slowly filling the interior from *Sahasrara Chakra* to *Mooladhara Chakra*. While exhaling slowly two syllables of OM i.e., O&M are to be pronounced. The sound is to be divided in two parts of timing ratio 2&1 i.e. 2/3 part of time pronounce 'O' & 1/3 time M.

Concentrate on sound, slowly exhale pronouncing O, for 2/3 of time exhalation and imagining sound travelling from *Mooladhara Chakra* to *Anaahata Chakra* through Sushumna along spinal cord. At this stage close the lips and pronounce M for 1/3 of time of the exhalation. The sound will be like that of humming of a honeybee. Imagine this sound travelling along imaginary line up to *Sahasrara Chakra* and complete the exhalation. With practice increase the duration of exhalations as much as you can.

Advantages: This is the basic sound calming nervous system and mind, improves concentration and activates spinal cord. It is very helpful in exciting *Agya Chakra*.

❑❑

6. Yogasanas

The aim is to keep both the mind and the body in perfect health through exercise of the body and the mind. The special feature of yogasanas is that what they do for the body, they do for the mind in a much more effective way. They are not only body-building exercises; more than that, they increase the mental powers. By achieving equanimity through asanas and pranayama, we control our senses as well as our breathing, which is capable of lengthening life-span. More elastic our limbs, more healthy we are. In fact, elasticity is life. The age between 35 and 60 years is such that many of our limbs start becoming stiff and lose their elasticity. It is therefore most essential to take care of the body during this period. The old-age diseases, such as heart attack, blood pressure and diabetes generally attack a man during this period. Those who do not want to lose the chance of keeping their youth intact and their body health in perfect order should invariably practise yogasanas daily, so that the elasticity of limbs is maintained and the mental faculties do not disintegrate.

The impurities, which are formed due to the wear and tear of the body and the accumulation of wastes after the food has been digested, find the foliowing outlets: (i) through the nose in breath, (ii) through the anus in the form of excreta, (iii) through urine, and (iv) through the skin in the form of perspiration and dirt. Diseases are caused in the body when the impurities get accumulated in it. It is very obvious that if all these outlets are clean and open, and the wastes find their outlet properly through them, we can never fall ill. The regular practice of yogasanas keeps these outlets clean and open, besides strengthening the organs which are responsible for excreting these impurities.

YOGASANAS are of two types: meditative and physical. Those involving mental activity are meditative, such as

Padmasana, *Siddhasana* and *Sukhasana*; and those which are done primarily for keeping the body fit are physical asanas.

While performing yogic postures keep in mind five essential principles (1) Bending of the body (2) Retaining the posture as per individual capacity (3) Control breathing (exhaling, chafing, inhaling, retention after inhaling as well as exhaling) (4) Concentration on portion of the body being stretched (5) Awareness about concentration centres. Practice of these principles increases effectiveness of the asanas and sequence of Pranayama is practised. Sometimes we retain the posture with breath exhaled, while some time inhaled, e.g. in *Paschimottana Asana* we reach final position while exhaling and concentrating on spinal region behind the naval area i.e., मनीपुर चक्र. In *Bhujanga Asana* we attain the posture while inhaling and concentrating on spinal area behind throat i.e., विशुद्धि चक्र.

The method mentioned above, when followed methodically with faith, makes breathing stabilised and controlled. This results in calming the mind. While cleaning the body asanas help calming the nervous system.

MEDITATIVE ASANAS

Padmasana (Lotus Pose)

Method: Place your left foot on the joint of your right

Padmasana

56

thigh, and the right foot on the joint of left thigh in such a way that both your heels touch each other below your navel in the middle of your abdomen. In this way, soles of your feet will stay on your thighs. Now, straighten your backbone and neck so that there is no bend at your waist. Place your hands on your knees.

Siddhasana (Perfect Pose)

Method: Place the heel of your left foot under the testes on the prostrate gland in such a way that the sole of your foot should touch your right thigh. Place the heel of your right foot against the pubic bone or just above the genitals. Now straighten your neck and backbone and raise your brows. Fix your attention on your eyebrows or on your breath. Place your hands as in *Padmasana.*

Siddhasana

Gyan-Mudra

Method: Sit in Padmasana or Siddhasana. Bend your index fingers (तर्जनी) and place them at the root of your thumbs. Spread the remaining three fingers forward, all joined together. Now put your hands on your knees with palms facing upwards.

57

Brahamanjli

Basic lotus pose with hand positioned in a manner that left palm touches back of right hand and both hands are placed below navel region in lap, facing upward.

One should sit in any of these asanas while practising *Dhyana*. The vertebral column, neck, head and waist should all be kept straight. These postures strengthen the nerves of the spinal cord and make them elastic; the sense organs are controlled; the respiration gets balanced; concentration increases; the movement of *Prana* in *Sushumna* is regulated because of the straight position of the spinal cord. That is why these asanas have been found most suitable for *Pranayama* and *Sadhana*.

Baddhapadmasana

Method: Sit in *Padmasana*. Try to project the feel as far out as possible. Now take the hands behind your back. Catch the right toes with your right hand and the left toes with your left hand. Keep the backbone straight as in *Padmasana*. Fix your gaze on the tip of your nose.

Advantages: It is very useful asana for the abdomen and the spine. It cures constipation, drowsiness, sleepishness, laziness, night-discharge and other semen troubles. It helps in curing T.B., asthma and cough. Disorders of the nervous system and the abdomen

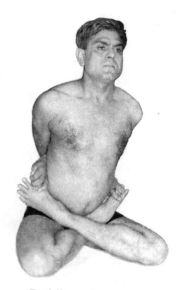

Baddhapadmasana

can be cured by its practice. It is particularly useful for women as it cures many disorders of the uterus. It also removes the flabbiness of their abdomen after childbirth. It calms down the mind and increases the power of concentration.

PHYSICAL ASANAS

These asanas are practiced for toning up various parts & glands of the body. Almost all the asanas have dynamic stage when we are reaching or returning from final position. The final position involving no movement is called static stage. The inhaling and exhaling is co-ordinate with dynamic stages and retention whereas normal breathing in restored during static stage of asana. Breathing cycle is mentioned in detail with each of the asana.

Trikonasana (Triangle Pose)

First Position: Stand erect, keeping the distance between the feet about one or one-and-a-half feet. Raise your right hand towards the sky and look towards its palm. Keep your left hand down. Now pull your right hand up and left hand down by stretching your body and inhaling.

Final Position: Now exhaling lower down slowly towards left, without bending your legs, in such a way that your left palm should touch the ground on the side of your foot. Keep on exhaling your breath during the process of lowering. Keeping your right arm close to your ear, make it parallel to the ground, looking all the time towards the sky. Now revert to the first position while inhaling the breath. In this position, stretch both your hands up and down.

Trikonasana

Repeat this process with your left hand up and right hand down.

59

Advantages: This asana helps the large intestine, liver and spleen in proper functioning. The muscles and nerves of the spinal cord become flexible while stretching. The muscles of the waist are strengthened. The neck and its glands also get good exercise.

Ardhachandrasana (Halfmoon Pose)

Method: Stand erect with joined heels. Take the hand above your head and join them in the posture of *namaskar*. Inhale and bend towards left from the waist. Exhale and bring the body back in the straight position. Repeat this by bending the body towards right. Concentrate on Manipúr chakra.

Ardhachandrasana

Advantages: In stretch-ing the muscles on both sides this asana makes the body flexible. It improves the functioning of the heart and the lungs. The liver, the stomach and the intestines are also strengthened by its practice. It improves digestion and increases appetite. It gives relief to those suffering from sciatica.

Suryanamaskara (Salutation to Sun)

There are 12 postures in this *kriya*. Before starting the *kriya*, stand erect with heels joined together and front of the feet a little apart.

1. Keep your folded hands in the posture of *namaskara* in the centre of your chest (*Hridaya Chakra*). The elbows should remain stretched outwards. Now recite the first of the *twelve mantras* given below. Concentrate on *Agya Chakra*.

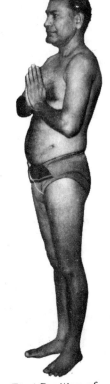

1. ओ३म् मित्राय नम:
2. ओ३म् सूर्याय नम:
3. ओ३म् रवये नम:
4. ओ३म् भानवे नम:
5. ओ३म् खगाय नम:
6. ओ३म् पूषणये नम:
7. ओ३म् हिरण्यगर्भाय नम:
8. ओ३म् मरीच्यै नम:
9. ओ३म् आदित्याय नम:
10. ओ३म् सावित्र्य नम:
11. ओ३म् अर्काय नम:
12. ओ३म् भास्कराय नम:

First Position of Suryanamaskara

2. While inhaling the breath, stretch your hands up and take them as far back as you can beyond your head. But your arms must remain straight and should touch your ears. Bend back your body from waist upwards as far as you can. Concentrate on *Vishuddhi Chakra*.

3. Now bring your arms forward from the front and bend your body down. Try to put the palms of your hands on the ground and place them beside your

61

Second and Eleventh Position of Suryanamaskara

Third and Tenth Position of Suryanamaskara

feet. In this state, try to touch the knees with your nose, without bending the knees. Exhale. Concentrate on *Manipur Chakra*.

4. Now take the left leg backward, bend your right knee and let it take position between the two arms, with the hands sticking to the ground. The hands and

Fourth and Ninth Position of Suryanamaskara

the right foot should be in one line. Now bend the neck as far backward as you can, throwing the chest out. Inhale. Concentrate on *Swadhistana Chakra*.

5. Exhale the breath and take your right leg also to the position of the left leg. Put your heels completely on the ground. Raise your hips upwards, touch your chest with your chin and look backward through your legs. Concentrate on *Sahasrara Chakra*.

Fifth and Eighth Position of Suryanamaskara

6. Place all your limbs on the ground except your hips which should be slightly raised from the ground. Your forehead, chest and knees should touch the ground. Make your breath normal.

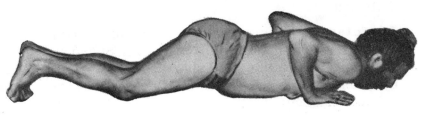

Sixth Position of Suryanamaskara

7. Now raise up the front portion of your body up to the chest, giving as little pressure on hands as you can. Inhale. Bend your neck as far back as you can. This posture is like *Bhujangasana*. Concentrate on *Mooladhara Chakra*.

Seventh Position of Suryanamaskara

8. The same position as in No. 5.
9. The same as in No. 4.
10. The same as in No. 3.
11. The same as in No. 2.
12. Finally, return to the position No. 1 and then take your hands down.

Thus, one *Suryanamaskara* is complete. In the next *Suryanamaskara*, the right leg will go backward instead of the left.

Advantages: *Suryanamaskara* is actually a composite exercise containing seven different asanas. Stomach, lungs, liver, spleen, intestines and spinal cord are strengthened by its regular practice. The entire body, specially the waist, gains in elasticity.

Practise *Shavasana* for a while after *Suryanamaskara*. The description of this asana has been given at the end of this chapter.

Rest Posture

While doing sitting asanas, practise 'rest posture' after every asana. This will normalise the breath and bring the stretched limbs, muscles and nerves to their original positions.

Rest Posture

Technique of Rest Posture: Raise your knees while sitting on your *dari* or blanket. Take your hands forward across the knees and hold the wrist of your left hand with your right hand; keep the arms resting on the knees. Close your eyes, keep your body loose and fix your mind on your breath. While doing an asana, one has to try to stretch one's limbs and achieve the full posture of the asana. But in this posture, one must leave the body in a completely relaxed state so that pure blood should circulate in the body and force the waste material out. This is the secret of health.

Tarasana (Palmyra Pose)

Method: Lie down on your back. Take your hands beyond your head and stretch them, keeping the palms facing the sky. Inhale and make your body stiff by stretching your hands upward and legs downward. The legs and feet should be close to each other. Relax the body and breath out.

Tarasana

65

Second Position: Interlock your fingers of both hands and stretch your body with hands upward and legs downward. Do this asana by retaining the breath in (*Antrik Kumbhaka*).

Advantages: It is very beneficial in increasing the height of the body. It is also very useful for those who walk with their spine bending forward. It removes the stiffness of the body and makes it supple. It improves the blood circulation system. It also helps in the proper functioning of the nervous system and the body retain its strength.

Naoasana (Boat Pose)

Method: Lie on ground with hands & feet as in TARASANA. While breathing-in raise feet, without bending knees & force toes to touch ground in area above the head & between two hands. From here, while breathing out return the feet back in starting position. At the same time swinging the upper portion of the body reach for the feet by hands & knees by head. Repeat the exercise five times. Throughout the exercise make sure knees do bend, toes stay stretched and concentration is on the spine which is being exercised.

Advantages: Increases flexibility of the spine and helps reduce obesity.

Kamar Chakra Asana (Twisting the Spine)

Method: While in sitting position place feet wide apart. While breathing out and without bending the knees, reach for feet or ankles, grip them with respective hand, pull the body forward. Try & touch the ground with forehead. Retain the position for a while. Breathing-in return to starting position. Now exhaling reach for the left foot with right hand, left knee with forehead & left hand going back till right hip joint. Inhaling return to starting position. Perform same sequence other side. Repeat these for five times on either side, before reaching for both feet & ground. Awareness about *Swadhistana Chakra* (below kidney area).

Kamar Chakra Asana

Advantages: Lumber region of spine is exercised. Fights obesity of hip and abdomen area. Improves functioning of digestive organism. Sciatica pain in legs is relieved. Seminal glands function is improved.

Janusirasana (Knee & Head Pose)

Stretch forward your right leg fully. Bend your left leg and place your left foot under your right thigh in such a way that its heel should touch your anus. Now raise your hands up while inhaling the breath. Bring them down slowly while exhaling, bending your body forward. Catch your left heel with both the palms of your hands. Try to touch your left knee with your nose or bring it as close to it as possible. Your elbows should rest on the ground.

Janusirasana

Stay in this position for some time and empty your lungs by exhaling while still in the position of *Bahya Kumbhaka*. If you desire to stay in this position a little longer, then breathe slowly. If you cannot touch your nose with the knee practise bending forward as far as you can.

This process should be repeated with the left leg stretched and right leg bent; try to touch your left knee now with your forehead. Concentrate on *Swadhistana Chakra*.

Advantages: This is a very useful posture for *Dhyana*. It helps to increase the concentration of mind. It also removes all seminal disorders. It brings elasticity and youthful agility in the entire body. It has a special effect in toning up the joints of knees, ankles and thighs. It is good for those suffering from sciatica.

Paschimottanasana (Posterior Stretch Pose)

Method: Sit on your *dari*, etc. Stretch your legs forward. Try to place the soles of your feet on the ground. Now raise your hands up in the sky slowly while inhaling. The palm's of your hands should point forward with your arms slightly touching the ears. Exhale and bring your hands down and catch hold of your heels. Pulling at the heels with your hands, place your elbows on the ground. You may now bury your face between the knees: If you cannot touch your knees

Paschimottanasana

68

with your nose or forehead, do not raise your knees. Instead, raise your bady a little while inhaling and then bring it down again while exhaling. Do this four or five times and you would see that after a few days, your body has become more elastic. Naw start inhaling and slowly raise your hands and body, and then sit in the rest posture. Concentrate on *Manipur Chakra*.

Advantages: It rouses the gastric fire and invigorates appetite. Disorders of the kidney, liver and spleen are removed. Obesity, piles, backache and constipation—all disappear with its regular practice. It helps strengthen *Sushumna Nadi* and increases the elasticity of the spine, thereby giving perennial youth.

Konasana (Angle Pose)

This is the counter pose of *Paschimottanasana* and should be practised after it.

Method: Stretch your legs forward and try to place the soles of your feet on the ground as far as possible. Place your hands on the ground beyond your waist. Start inhaling and while doing it raise your body, putting its weight mostly on hands. Bend your neck backward and try to put the soles of your feet fully on the ground. Look backwards and raise your chest up. Concentrate on *Manipur Chakra*.

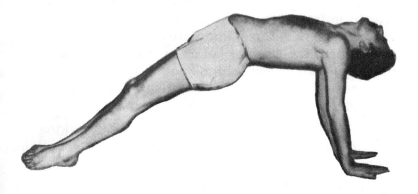

Konasana

69

Advantages: It strengthens the shoulders and relieves abdominal stiffness. The spine gets strength and the entire nervous system is toned up.

Akaran Dhanurasana (Archer's Pose)

Method: Stretch your legs forward. Bend your right leg and place its heel on the left thigh. Now make a ring with the thumb and index finger of your right hand and catch the toe of your left foot with it. In a similar way, catch the toe of your right foot with your left hand. Lift your right leg and take it near your right ear. Inhale slowly

Akaran Dhanurasana

while doing so. Do not bend your waist. Keep your face straight in front. Be careful not to turn your face and to bring your right ear near your lifted foot. You have to take the foot near the ear and not *vice versa*. Keep yourself in this position for a few seconds and in this duration keep your breath inside (*Antrik Kumbhaka*). Slowly go back to the original position and exhale.

The same process should be repeated by taking the right toe near the left ear. Concentrate on *Mooladhara Chakra*.

Advantages: This asana is particularly useful for those with desk jobs. It strengthens the lungs, liver and large

70

intestine. The muscles of the waist and shoulders also get strength and energy.

Yogamudra

Method: Assume the posture of *Padmasana* and let your heels meet below your navel. Take your hands at your back and catch the wrist of your left hand with your right hand. Close your left fist. Now straighten your back and raise your shoulders; your hands should exert their force downward. Inhale slowly. Bend your body forward from the waist in such a way that your backbone remains straight. While doing so keep exhaling. Do not bend your neck nor raise your hips from the ground. Touch the ground with your forehead, raising your locked hands high in the sky. Practise staying in this posture for some time; inhale and exhale slowly. From here, return to your original position, while slowly inhaling. Concentrate on *Manipur Chakra*.

Now repeat this process by first turning your waist towards right and then towards left. The hands in the former position will be on the left hip and in the latter position an the right: In the former case, the forehead would touch the ground beside the right knee and in the latter case beside the left knee. Be sure to turn your waist as much as you can.

Open your *Padmasana* and come to the rest posture.

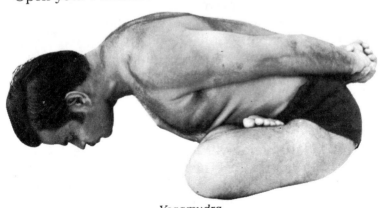

Yogamudra

Advantages: The impurities stuck in the legs and joints leave their place and the muscles get strengthened. Digestive organs become healthy; the stomach, liver and spleen are toned up; constipation is removed. The spine and the nerve tissues originating from it as well as the muscles of the waist get strengthened.

Garbhasna (Embryo Pose)

Method: Sit in *Padmasana*. Insert your arms through the openings between your calfs and thighs, so that the elbows come out below the thighs. Now sit on your hips and place the hands on the ears. Keep the head and the back straight.

Advantages: This is one of the most useful asanas for women. Its regular practice helps to keep all the uterus disorders away. It strengthens the womb and is particularly recommended for those women who give birth to weak, deformed or dead children. It is equally good for men as it increases flexibility and gives youthful vigour to all the organs. It provides relief in gout and arthritis cases. This posture helps in gaining control over senses and the mind.

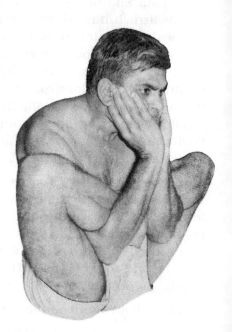

Garbhasana

Gorakshasana

First Position: Bend your legs and join the soles of your feet. Place the joined heels under your genitals (at the place between your anus and penis or vagina). Make a grip of your hands like a comb and catch the front portion of

Gorakshasana

your feet. Your both thumbs should take position on your toes. While keeping your spine straight, try to touch the ground with knees or should be as near the ground as possible. Fill your breath in. Make your arms also straight. Stop the breath inside for some time. Stay in this position as long as possible without exhaling. Then return to the position of rest while exhaling slowly. Concentrate on *Swadhistana Chakra.*

Second Position: In the second stage, sit on your heels and place your hands on your knees. Press your knees to the ground with your hands, keeping your waist and face straight. Stay in this position for some time, then go to the state of rest.

Advantages: Seminal glands get good exercise by this asana. It transmutes the seminal energy, and is particularly useful for those suffering from wet-dreams. It also cures the ailments of genito-urinary system.

Second Position of Gorakshasana

Gomukhasana (Cow Head Pose)

Method: Fold your left leg. Place the heel of the left foot under your left hip. Now fold the right leg over the left buttock in such a manner that the heel of your right foot is placed near your left hip. Take your right arm behind your back from above and left arm from below, so that fingers of both the hands are interlocked behind the back. Stay in this position for some time. Then repeat this

Gomukhasana

74

by folding the right leg and placing its heel under the right hip. Concentrate on *Anahata Chakra*.

Advantages: This gives strength to the knees, shins and feet. It prevents disorders of the semen and prevents any enlargement of the testicles. It is also beneficial for the nervous system, lungs and heart.

Ardhamatsyendrasana

Method: Bend your right leg at the knee and set the heel between your anus and penis or vagina. Now lift your left foot and crossing it over the right knee, place it on the ground on the outer side of the right thigh.

The entire sole of the left foot should be on the ground. Adjust it in such a way that your left knee should remain in the middle of your chest. Now lift your right hand straight up; bring

Ardhamatsyendrasana

it down slowly crossing the left knee, and catch the sole of your left foot from the side of the toe with this hand. The left hand will go at the back. Keep the spine straight and look backward. Inhale and turn your spine fully, so that both the shoulders come in a straight line. The more you

75

turn the spine, the greater the benefit, because you are pressing your left knee on your stomach and chest. You will press it more as much as you turn your spine. The pressing of the knee influences your abdomen, pancreas, spleen and large intestine on the one side and liver and large intestine on the other. Both the kidneys and the small intestine are also strengthened. Be careful not to bend your waist. If your hand does not reach the sole of your foot, hold your ankles instead or press your knee a little more with your elbow.

The speciality of this asana lies in the pressing of the abdomen by the knee and also in turning the waist and the shoulders so that one looks backward.

Repeat this posture by placing the left heel between the anus and the genitals, and by pressing the abdomen with the right knee.

Advantages: This asana makes the spine elastic and tones up the nervous system along with the spinal nerve-roots. This is specially advantageous for those suffering from diabetes. All kinds of backaches are cured by its practice. The digestive organs, specially the pancreas and the liver, become strong. The lungs and heart are also toned up.

Matsyendrasana

Method: Fold your left leg from the knee and place it on the right thigh as is done in the *Padmasana*. The sole of the left foot will be set at the root of the thigh. Now lift the right foot and keep it on the other side of the left knee. Raise the left hand, take it over the right knee and catch the right toe firmly in the left hand. Take your right hand behind the back, so that the chin touches the left shoulder. Turn back as much as possible. Stay in this position. Come back and relax. Repeat it on the other side placing the right foot on the left thigh.

Advantages: It is a useful asana for stomach problems and is the best asana for combatting diabetes. It cures

Matsyendrasana

enlargement of spleen and has a very good effect on the pancreas and liver. It used to be a favourite asana of yogi Matsyendranath. The hathayogis still like to practise this asana for yogic powers.

Vajrasana
(Hardy Pose)

Method: Bend your legs and sit on your knees by placing your heels under your hips. The heels should be open but the toes should be joined and the feet

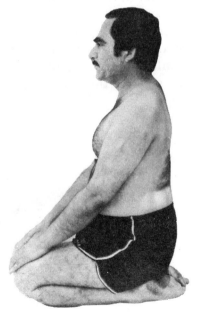

Vajrasana

would be all on the ground. Now make your spine straight, place your hands on your knees while keeping the arms straight. You can sit in this posture at any time of the day even after eating your food or after travelling a long distance. This will give rest to your tired legs. You can practise it while reading also. This asana is as useful as it is easy.

Advantages: This asana has good effect on our digestive system. The impurities accumulated in our shins and knees are displaced.

Suptavajrasana (Horizontal Hardy Pose)

Method: First sit in *Vajrasana*. Now stand up on your knees and set your feet apart, so that you can sit on the ground between them. The feet will again be in lying position. Place your hands on the front part of your feet. Bend backward and let your elbows rest on the ground one by one. Hang your neck backward so that your eyes are also pointed backwards. In the final stage, lower the whole of your back on the ground. Stretch your hands backward while inhaling. Now remove the gap between your knees if there is any. Stay in this position for a little while. Then lock your fingers and make a cushion of your hands under your head. Normalise your breath and stay in this posture for one or two minutes.

Suptavajrasana (First Position)

This is rather a difficult posture. If you are unable to do according to the instructions above, practise with a gap between the knees in the beginning. Your body will take some time to gain elasticity and then you would find it easy to do. While coming back from this asana, first remove your hands from beneath your head, sit on the elbows turn by turn while keeping your eyes on your knees. Concentrate on *Manipur Chakra*.

Suptavajrasana (Second Position)

Advantages: The knees, thighs, waist, abdomen, spine, neck and ankles are strengthened. The kidneys and the organs of procreation, in both the women and men, are toned up. It relieves hot temper and physical and mental exhaustion.

Shashankasana

Method: Sit in *Vajrasana*. Inhale and raise both the hands up above the head. The palms should point forward. Exhale and place the hands on the ground while bending slowly from the waist. The forehead should also touch the ground a little away from the knees. Stay in this posture for at least one minute and then relax completely. Concentrate on *Agya Chakra*.

Advantages: This is the reverse posture of *Suptavajrasana* and should invariably be performed after it. This is an asana of relaxation. It calms the disturbed mind

Shashankasana

and gives strength and energy to the brain. Negative feelings of anger, hatred, etc., are gradually relieved by its constant practise.

Mayurasana (Peacock Pose)

'Mayura' means peacock. So, this may be called the peacock posture as the body in this asana resembles a peacock.

Method: Sit on your knees. Bend a little forward, join your elbows together and rest your palms on the ground. Keep a distance of 3 or 4 cm between your wrists. Keep the hands firm. Now bring down your abdomen slowly on your

Mayurasana

80

joined elbows. Balancing the weight of the entire body on the elbows, stretch your legs. Now inhale and lift your face in the front and your legs in the rear from the ground and try to make them parallel to the ground. Your head and legs should be in level with each other. Stay in this posture for a few moments, then put your feet on the ground first and exhale.

Rest for a few minutes in *Shavasana* after this. This is a rather difficult posture. In the beginning, balance yourself only for a little while. Be careful to keep your elbows joined together. After you have had enough practice, do it for one or two minutes daily. Concentrate on *Manipur Chakra*.

Advantages: It enhances the working power of the kidneys and the digestive organs and removes all the disorders of wind, bile and phlegm. It increases blood circulation in the body and purifies the blood. This gives beauty and *oja* to the body. Sluggishness of the liver and hepatic torpidity are removed. This also helps to check obesity.

Ushtrasana
(Camel Pose)

'Ushtra' is a Sanskrit word, which means camel. This asana is therefore called camel posture.

Method: First sit in *Vajrasana* posture and stand up on your knees. Gradually separate your knees until they are about 25 to 30 cm apart. Now place your hands on your waist in such a way that your fingers

Ushtrasana

81

should be towards your abdomen and your thumbs on your kidneys towards your back. In this state, throw your neck back and also bend backward from your waist. When the bend is complete, take your hands off your waist and put them on the soles of your feet. Throw your abdomen outwards from the front and your neck as far back as possible. Stay in this position for some time and take breath in a normal way. While coming back, place your hands on your waist and stand erect on your knees. Then sit in the rest posture.

Advantages: It has a good effect on the glands of the neck. The fatness of the belly and waist are gradually removed and the body becomes more elastic. It corrects the digestive system and removes the disorders of the abdomen. It gives energy to the chest and the lungs, and checks *tridosha.*

Shithilasana

Method: Lie down on your stomach, keeping your face towards right. Bend your right arm from the elbow so that the fingers of your right hand come near your nose at a distance of about 15 cm. Bend your right leg a little so that your right foot should come near your left knee. Your entire belly and chest should touch the ground and the body should be left in a completely relaxed position. There should be absolutely no stiffness in any part of the body. Breathe slowly and deeply, keeping your attention on your breath.

Shithilasana

Repeat this posture with your left cheek on the ground and your left arm and leg bent. On the ground, the body should be in such a relaxed state as if a child is sleeping in the lap of his mother. Close your eyes and feel as if you are also sleeping in the lap of Mother Nature.

Bhujangasana (Cobra Pose)

Method: Lie on stomach, toes, heals and legs together with soles facing upwards. Forehead on the ground. Hands placed near respective shoulder, palms facing down, tips of fingers in line with top of the rounded shoulders. The elbows along the sides of the body, touching ground and the body. Move the nose and chin forward, bending back the nape of the neck. Inhaling raise the head and upper portion of the body. Lower half of the body i.e., stomach & legs stay on ground. By pressing ground with hands try to raise the upper portion little more, straightening the elbows slightly. Hold the position for 15 to 20 seconds, breathe normally. Inhale and return while exhaling. Relax in *Shithilasana* to the right. Concentrate on *Vishuddhi Chakra*.

Bhujangasana

Advantages: It is specially a useful asana for the kidneys. The neck, shoulders and spine get strength. The glands of the neck and tonsils get influenced favourably. The body gets youthful elasticity. It causes an abundant flow of blood towards the backbone. It is a very useful asana for strengthening the heart.

Sarpasana (Running Snake Pose)

Method: Lie on the stomach, feet together and hands held at the back with fingers interlocked. Breath in, raise the legs, knees and upper position of the body and roll on the stomach a few times, followed by rest in *Shithilasana*.

Sarpasana

Advantages: Improves balance of the body, fights obesity, helps in constipation and improves appetite.

Naukasana (Canoe Pose)

Method: Lie on stomach with feet together and hands above the head. Breathing-in raise feet, hands and head. Rock on stomach while concentrating on *Manipur Chakra*.

Naukasana

Advantages: Massages digestive system, fights obesity.

Shalabhasana (Locust Pose)

The word 'shalabha' means locust. In this posture, the body assumes the form of a locust.

Method: Lie down on the ground with your face downward. Join your heels and keep your feet on the ground. Your chin should rest on the ground. Place your hands under your thighs in such a way that the palms should stick to the thighs. Now raise your legs and the hind portion of your body up to the waist, while inhaling. Do not bend you legs nor raise your face from the ground. Stay in this position for sometime and then come back slowly exhaling the breath and taking your hands out. Concentrate on *Anahata Chakra.*

Shalabhasana

Relax and loosen your body, while keeping your right cheek on the ground.

Advantages: All parts of the abdomen get fully exercised. It keeps the heart, spine and lungs healthy and strong. It saves us from the diseases of the heart. Obesity is also cured.

Dhanurasana (Bow Pose)

Method: The word 'dhanu' in Sanskrit means bow. The body resembles a bow in this asana.

Lie down on the ground with your face downward. Inhale deeply. Bend your legs and grasp your ankles with your hands, keeping all the five fingers of your each hand on the inner side of the legs. First raise the hind part of

85

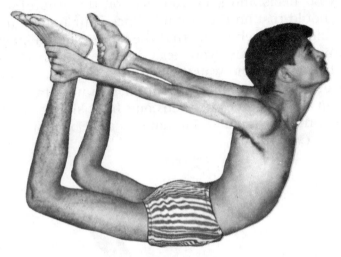

Dhanurasana

the body and then raise your chest also. Bend your neck backwards and look at the sky. There should be a tug of war between the legs and hands, so that your entire body comes to rest on your navel. Bend your body in a bow shape. Slowly come back to the original position while exhaling the breath, and relax in *Shithilasana* on the right side. Concentrate on *Swadhistana Chakra*.

Advantages: This asana provides full exercise to the spine which becomes more elastic. It benefits the kidneys. Entire digestive area is stretched, by which abdominal disorders are cured. It also provides sufficient exercise to the neck, ribs and lungs. It helps remove obesity. It helps cure menstruation and uterus disorders. The heart becomes strong.

Padauttanasana (Raised Feet Pose)

Method: Lie on the back. Feet together. Hands by the side. Stretch the body and toes. Breathing-in raise the feet upto 3 inches and hold the position for few seconds and return. After a while repeat the exercise by raising the feet about 1 foot off the ground. Hold for few seconds and return to rest.

86

Padauttanasana

Advantages: First position helps activate digestive system and regenerative organism. Second position energises digestive system near navel area i.e., small intestine etc. Improves appetite.

Hastpadottanasana (Hand Foot Raised Pose)

Method: Lie down on your back. Take your hands beyond your head and stretch them, keeping the palms facing the sky. Now make your body stiff by stretching your hands upward and your legs downward. Raise your legs up, about 7 or 8 cm from the ground. Slowly raise your left leg and bring it at 90^0 to the ground while inhaling. Now raise your right arm, and try to touch the raised leg, while exhaling. Do not raise your head nor there be any bend in your raised leg. Stay in this position for a few moments.

Hastpadottanasana (First Position)

Bring the leg slowly dawn to its original position and inhale. Bring the arm also to its original position on the ground and exhale.

Repeat this by raising your right leg and left arm. But do not put your legs down during the process. Keep them raised at a distance of about 7 or 8 cm from the ground.

Now raise both your legs while inhaling. While they are at 90° to the ground, raise both your arms slowly and exhale. Try to touch your toes with your hands. Stay in this position for sometime. Then bring the legs and the hands down. Relax. Concentrate on *Swadhistana Chakra*.

Hastpadottanasana (Second Position)

Advantages: This is the best and sure remedy for obesity. Abdominal disorders are cured. Even chronic constipation is removed. Spine, shoulders and the muscles of the back are strengthened. This is very useful asana for increasing height. It increases appetite and cures backache.

Makarasana (Crocodile Pose)

First Posture: Lie down on your back. Bend your legs in such a way that your heels should touch your hips. Keep a distance of about 15 cm between your feet.

Now spread your hands to your right and left sides in such a manner that the palms should face the sky. Keep the body completely stretched. Now start inhaling; turn both of your knees to right and try to place them on the ground. Simultaneously, turn your neck towards left and look towards your left palm. Wring your body like a towel. Stay in this position for some time. Then return to the original position while exhaling.

Repeat the process by turning the knees to left and the neck to right. After this asana, lie down in *Shavasana*.

Makarasana (First Position)

Second Posture: Stretch your hands to your sides in line with your shoulders, palms facing upward and the fist closed. Join your feet and legs and raise them up to an angle of 60°. Take your feet towards right and bend your neck to the left. Inhale and wring your body fully like a towel, keeping your eyes on your left fist. Bring back your legs again at 60° and exhale. Face also will come to its original position.

Makarasana (Second Position)

89

Repeat this process by taking your legs to left and your neck to right. Relax in *Shavasana*.

Advantages: It increases the circulation of blood in the body and relieves the body exhaustion. It particularly has good effect on the abdomen. The back and neck are exercised and their elasticity brings back youth and beauty to the body.

Pawanamuktasana (Wind Liberating Pose)

Method: Lie down on your back and stretch both your legs. Now leaving the left leg stretched on the ground bend your right leg at the knee and bring the bent knee near the chest. Now inhale and press your bent leg on your chest with both hands, which should be interlocked for

Pawanamuktasana (First Position)

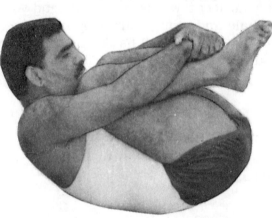

this purpose. Keep the breath full in your belly and go on pressing the leg on it. Stay in this position for some time. Now start exhaling, lift your head and try to touch your bent knee with your nose. Inhale and

Pawanamuktasana (Second Position)

bring your head back in the normal position; also take the leg down and exhale. Concentrate on *Manipur Chakra*.

Repeat this process with your right leg and then with both the legs.

Advantages: This asana regulates the wind in the body. It brings the wind down, so that it can be easily exhausted through the anus. The wind then does not cause disorders in the stomach, and constipation is also relieved. It also helps in keeping away the diseases of the lungs and the heart. Obesity and excessive fat of the abdomen also diminish.

Caution: Pregnant women are prohibited from doing this asana.

Chakrasana (Wheel Pose)

Method: Lie down on your back. Bring your heels near your thighs by bending your legs at the knees. Keep a little distance between your feet. Now bring each of your hands by the sides of each shoulder. Place them in such a way that the palms should rest on the ground and the direction of the fingers should be towards your feet. First raise your hips and waist and take your knees a little forward. Put pressure on your hands and feet, and lift your back, neck and head also. Try to reduce the distance between your hands and feet by bringing them closer to each other. Your neck would hang

Chakrasana

91

at the back and your shoulders would be raised. In this way, your body will get the shape of a *chakra* or wheel. To take full advantage of this asana, lessen the distance between your hands and feet as much as possible. Concentrate on *Manipur Chakra*.

Advantages: This asana makes the spine elastic, relieves backache, strengthens the muscles of the shoulders, chest and abdomen. Women get relief from pain during their menstruation periods. It also cures shakiness of hands, neck and head.

Upasana

Method: It is a reverse posture of *Chakrasana*. Lie down on your back. First stretch your feet outward and then raise your legs straight upto 45°. Now raise your back and try to touch the feet with your hands straight. Only the buttocks should be on the ground. Now leave the feet and stay in this position for some time. Concentrate on *Manipur Chakra*.

Upasana

Advantages: As it is a reverse posture, it brings the nervous system in natural position. Balance of the body is maintained. It reduces the paunch and cures constipation.

Halasana (Plough Pose)

Method: In this posture the body resembles the shape of plough (*hala*). Lie down on your back and stretch your body. Keep your arms by your sides along the hips. The palms will face the ground. Putting pressure on your hands, lift your legs slowly and make with them an angle of 90⁰ at your waist. Head should not be lifted at all, nor should there be any bend in the legs. The feet will remain completely stretched. Put more pressure on the hands, lift your waist also and take your legs beyond your head with feet touching the ground. In this position, your knees should go beyond your head. In the entire process, the legs will remain joined, the hands will stick to the ground, and breathing should remain normal. The legs should be lifted as slowly as possible. Do not do any violence to your body.

Halasana

Now lift your hands from the ground and take them to the back of your head, so that they might touch the toes of your feet. Bring your legs back to the 90⁰ angle very slowly, stay here for a few seconds and then place the legs down on the ground. Relax completely in *Shavasana*.

The beginners should raise legs only up to 90⁰ at the waist and then come back. Increase the frequency slowly; do it 3 or 4 times daily. Concentrate on *Vishuddhi Chakra*.

Advantages: *Halasana* is very useful for increasing mental and physical energy. It helps in the supply of the fresh blood to the spine and its ligaments; abdominal cavity is compressed and fresh blood enters this region. It also gives strength to pancreas, spleen, kidneys and liver. It removes fat from the abdominal region and the waist. It helps to cure backache and fatigue of legs. It also increases memory and elasticity.

Sarvangasana (Shoulder Stand)

Method: Lie down on your back. Stretch your body in a state of alert, your hands on the side of the thighs, palms resting on the ground. As in the case of *Halasana*, raise your legs slowly while putting pressure on your hands. Start inhaling. Bring your legs to a 45⁰ angle and stay a while in this position. Then bring them at 90⁰ and stay for a few moments. Now raise your waist also and take the legs beyond your head, making them parallel to the ground; exhale while doing so. Lift your hands from the ground, bend the arms from the elbows, put your hands on your back, and raise your legs upward with your

Sarvangasana

elbows resting on the ground and your hands supporting your back. In this position, your chin should bury itself into your chest; your entire body from feet to shoulders should be erect. Breathe in the normal way.

After sufficient practice, one can stay in this position up to ten minutes. While returning from this position, do not give any jerks to the body. Come back as slowly as possible. Remove the support of your hands from the back, make the legs parallel to the ground as before, put the back on the ground, bring your legs at 90^0 on your waist, take them down slowly, stop them at about 8 cm from the ground, open them a little sideways and place them on the ground without any jerk. Relax in *Shavasana*. Concentrate on *Vishuddhi Chakra*.

Advantages: It helps in activating the blood flow towards the neck and head. All our body organs in this region are nourished and strengthened. As the name suggests, it in fact gives nourishment and strength to all parts of the body. The disorders of the thyroid, tonsils, neck, lungs and ears are removed. The strength of the brain and the nerves is increased, eye sight is improved, wind is controlled and blood purified. Headaches and jaundice are checked. Through the proper functioning of the thyroid, it improves the functioning of all parts of the body. The circulatory, respiratory and alimentary systems of the body get great strength. It makes the spine elastic and provides youthful vigour.

Matsyasana (Fish Pose)
The word 'matsya' in Sanskrit means fish. The body resembles a fish in this posture. It should be practised after *Sarvangasana*, because it is a counter pose of *Sarvangasana*.

Method: Lie down on your back. Do *Padmasana* while lying down. Let the knees remain on the ground. Raise your head, making an arc with the chest. Now place the middle of your head on the ground and look backward. In this position, a sort of bridge will be created between your head and waist, with your chest rising up. Now grasp the toes of your feet with your hands, resting your elbows on the ground. Inhale. Stretch your limbs fully. Stay in this position for sometime. Now leave your toes, put your elbows on the ground and with their support raise the upper portion of the body. Staying in this position, move your

Matsyasana

neck from left to right, right to left, clockwise and anti-clockwise. Come back slowly, open your *Padmasana* and relax in *Shavasana*. Concentrate on *Agya Chakra*.

New adepts may not be able to perform this asana in lotus pose. They may lie on back, slide hands under the hips, palms facing the ground and legs straight & together. Taking the help of elbows, raise upper portion of the body and look towards the feet. Breathing-in tilt the head back so that top of the head rests on ground, with shoulders and shoulder blades off the ground. After a while straighten the back, take hands out from under the body taking

Simple Position of Matsyasana

96

support of the elbow, raise body to half inclined position and carryout neck relaxing movements i.e., forward, sideways & rotation.

Advantages: This asana relieves the stiffness caused in the neck because of *Sarvangasana*. It invigorates pituitary gland, which keeps the development of the body balanced. The neck, face, lungs and heart get nourishment. The muscles of the waist and abdomen get exercise; constipation is removed.

Shirshasana (Head Stand)

Standing on one's head is called *Shirshasana*. Due to its great benefits it is called 'the king of asanas'. It is rather a difficult asana. So, it should be attempted when one has mastered other asanas. It is also essential to take due care and precautions in doing asana, because wrong posture may result in very harmful effects on the body. It is therefore recommended that it should be done under the guidance of an accomplished teacher. It is also important to remember that the beginners should never do it beyond one or two minutes. In fact, nobody should do it beyond his capacity. It is also advised that

First Position of Shirshasana

this asana should be done after doing other asanas. Moreover, *Shirshasana*, should always be followed by *Shavasana*.

Do this asana in three stages:

First Stage: Fold your blanket four times to make it thick and soft. However, the folded blanket should be big enough

97

to easily accommo-date your head and arms. Now fold the knees and bend on this blanket. Interlock your fingers in the shape of a cup. Place the hands on the blanket with your elbows resting on the blanket. Next place the crown of your head on the blanket in such a way that the back of crown touches your cupped palms. It is necessary to place the elbows properly on the blanket as the balance is achieved on their firm stand. Now bring the knees closer to the chest, make the back straight so that the front portion of the feet touches the ground. Keep the knees folded and the heels near the hips. Stay in this position for a few seconds. It would be better if this practice is repeated for a few days before attempting the final posture of *Shirshasana*

Second Stage: When you are confident of staying in this position steady, attempt to straighten the body up to the knees. The heels will still remain with the hips. Practice this stage also for a few days, but do not strain yourself. If possible, ask someone to help you in achieving the balance.

Third Stage: In this third stage raise your legs up. The body should be kept straight up, but there should be no undue stretching of the legs. The idea is to let the blood flow freely. One should breathe slowly and deeply through one's nose in this posture.

At the start, the duration of this posture should not be more that 30 seconds. Increase the duration very gradually. But do it always according to

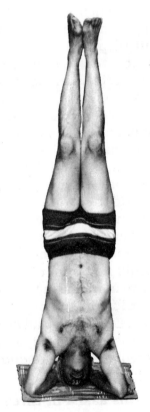

Third Position of Shirshasana

98

your capacity. Whenever you feel any discomfort, come back to relax and rest.

Come back to the original position as slowly as you did while attaining the final posture. It would be better if you come back in three stages. Do not bring the legs down with a jerk. Lower the legs down, fold the knees, slowly draw the knees close to the body and place the toes on the ground. Keep the toes on the ground and raise the head from the ground.

After doing *Shirshasana*, stand straight for about 30 seconds to prevent the sudden downward flow of blood which can be harmful. In the end, do *Shavasana* for at least two minutes, so that blood supply to all the parts of the body becomes regulated. Concentrate on *Agya Chakra*.

Caution: (i) Do not perform this assana beyond your capacity. The moment you feel discomfort, come back to the initial position slowly. (ii) Those suffering from high blood pressure should not do this asana. (iii) Those suffering from eyes, nose and ear diseases are also advised not to attempt it. (iv) Heart patients are forbidden to do it.

Advantages: This asana is of paramount importance for the health and vitality of all the parts of the body. All the body systems are strengthened by its practice—the circulatory system, the digestive system, the respiratory system, the nervous system and the excretory system. They become healthy and strong. It is however of greatest benefit to the brain as it helps give nourishment to all its cells and tissues by reversing the blood supply. Premature graying of hair is stopped by its practice. The skin becomes bright and smooth and the face becomes radiant. Advantages are similar to *Sarvangasana* which is better for elders and irregular sadhak.

Shavasana (Dead Body Pose)
Method: Lie on your back and let your body relax campletely. Let your feet be 30 to 40 cm apart, your arms on your sides with palms upwards, eyes gently closed with

attention on breathing. Keep your body in a straight position; the legs, hands and neck should have no curves or bends, so that the blood flows through all parts of the body freely and without any obstruction. Breathe deeply and effortlessly in a natural way.

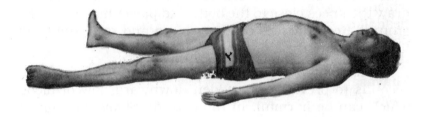

Shavasana

Other asanas usually dislocate our breath, increase our speed of breathing. When *Shavasana* is done after any other asana, it makes our breathing normal, provides necessary rest to our limbs and gives us strength to be ready for the next asana. When breathing is normalised, take a long and deep breath. Now concentrate on each and every part of your body, putting it in a completely relaxed state. There should be absolutely no tension in your body or mind. Only then you can consider this asana properly done. If there are thoughts in the mind, they should be removed. Repeat the word 'Om' mentally to get concentration of mind. Make your mind completely vacant and stay in this position for some time.

Second Position of Shavasana

Of all the asanas, *Shavasana* is the most difficult one. To do it successfully, one needs a lot of practice.

We can do it lying on our sides also instead of lying on our back. For this, lie down on your left or right side and bending your left or right arm (according to the side on which you are lying) from the elbow, place it under your head like a pillow. Bend your knees a little. The rest of the body will remain in a straight line. Apply this posture to the left for better digestion.

Shavasana should also be performed in following three stages:

1. Relax complete body. Move your feet to remove any tension and relax nerves in the feet. Move shoulders to loosen them and relax upper portion of the body. Similarly move neck to relax nerves in the head. Convince your mind that complete body is relaxed.

2. Breathe normally and visualize the breathing to be in tension free state. This will result in state of relaxation.

3. With closed eyes, let your concentration be focussed on limbs, starting from toes to top of the head. This travel along the limbs should be like another person is inspecting your body limb by limb. Such a sequence results in tension free mind & body.

Note: Do *Shavasana* after each asana or leave the body loose and relaxed for some time. Whenever you feel physically or mentally exhausted, practise it for a few minutes. You will get relief. If you do not get sound sleep, practise it before sleeping.

Advantages: This asana puts new life in a battered body and mind. The stiffness of tissues and restlessness of mind can be easily removed by it. When we do *Shavasana* after another asana, the blood reaches the depth of each tissue and nerve, so that impurities are washed off, lungs purify more blood. This asana provides relief in diseases like blood pressure, weakness of nerves and other mental ailments. This cures bad temper also.

Singhasana (Roar)

Method: This calls for roaring like a lion. Sit in *Padmasana*. Put your knees on the ground and lean on your hands; face towards the sun, the waist bent downward; open your mouth and let the rays of the sun enter it; take out your tongue, fix your eyes on the tip of your nose and roar as a lion would do.

Singhasana

Advantages: This asana is very useful in curing the ailments of the throat and chest. Tonsils are cured and lungs are toned up.

Yognidra

After a daily routine of *Yogasana* try and rest for half an hour. The static electric energy and heat energy created during the exercise activate body cells and one gets a feeling of freshness physically and mentally. Modern medical science accepts that a cleaned body and calm mind can act as curative force for many diseases.

In *Yognidra* conscious effort in made to direct mind and body towards state of rest and relaxation. An adept practices to pass instructions, like auto suggestion, to parts of the body and mind to relax and reach tension free state.

Method: To practice *Yognidra*, lie down in *Shavasana*, eyes closed, concentrate on breathing cycle. Calm the breathing to be fully relaxed physically. Starting from this state you can practice *Yognidra* for 10 to 45 minutes.

After lying down in this state for about two minutes direct your awareness to right toes. Move them on by one and together to loosen and relax them. Move the foot, sole, ankle, calf muscle, knee, thigh and hip joint, loosen them to relax. Similarly relax left leg from toes to hip joint. Feel that both legs have become listless & relaxed and imagine that circulatory system has no impediment and dirty blood is travelling towards the heart freely. Now direct your attention towards right hand. Move all the fingers one by one and relax them. Similarly palm, wrist, forearm, elbow, upperarm and shoulder should be instructed to relax. Repeat the sequence on left hand & relax it. Both arms & legs are now in state of tension free existence.

After immobilising arms & legs direct your concentration towards digestive system and visualise important organs & their functioning. Coming upward concentrate on left lung and visualise functioning of the heart and flow of polluted blood to lungs & purified blood stream to heart & rest of the body. Breathe deeply and visualise circulatory system functioning in lungs & heart.

Spine controls almost all functions of the body through nervous system. Therefore concentrate on each vertebrae of the spine in a sequence. Combine *Ida*, *Pingla* and *Sushumna* with the spine and visualise the complete system. Visualize remaining organs like neck area, jaw, tongue, teeth, nose, eyes and ears. Close the eyes and make effort to relax them. Concentrate on the brain area inside the skull and try to feel the relaxed state.

Experience this relaxed state of complete body and visualise that all toxins are being expelled through respiration, sweat glands, urinary & excretory tracts. All other functions are regulated and co-ordinated, complete body is becoming free of all toxins.

Continue to lie is this state for a while. The breathing process be made centre of your concentration. While inhaling visualize that energy from environment is entering your lungs and while exhaling visualise that toxins, in the form of carbon dioxide are being expelled and your body

103

is becoming healthier. After experiencing calmed respiration for a while slowly move the body and get up.

Laughter

Laughing without inhibitions is very essential for our health. We live in a world of tensions and mental worries. If we laugh without restraint, both the tension of mind and exhaustion of body are removed. The body gets new strength, bad temper is relieved and we feel interested in our work. There are three ways of doing it.

(a) **Laughing with mouth shut:** Keeping your mouth shut and without making any sound, laugh internally. You will feel that each and every limb of your body is laughing. This has a special effect on toning up the intestines.

(b) **Laughing without sound:** You will now laugh with your mouth open, but there would be no sound. This has also toning up effect on lungs and digestive system. Headache is cured.

(c) **Laughing loudly:** Laugh loudly with open mouth in convulsive merriment. Do it five times. This will provide excellent exercise for your lungs and abdomen. The intestines will be toned up.

❑❑

7. Pranayama

Many people equate *Prana* with air or breath and, therefore, define *Pranayama* as the exercise of breathing. But this concept is wrong and misleading. *Prana*, in fact, is the vital energy which pervades each and every element of the world, whether organic or inorganic. It is, no doubt, related to the air and breath. But *Prana* is not only the air; it is the vital energy in the air. While talking of *Pranayama*, we should always keep in mind the difference between the air and the vital energy within it. The word meaning of *Pranayama* is the "expansion of prana." The aim of *Pranayama* is to inspire, infuse, control, regulate and balance the *Prana Shakti* (vital energy) in the body.

Just as bathing is necessary for the purification of the body, similarly *Pranayama* is essential for the purification of the mind. *Pranayama* helps to improve retention power and concentration power. This in turn leads to soundness of mind and soundness of body. The liver, the stomach, the kidneys, the intestines, the digestive organs, the veins and the entire nervous system get strengthened by the regular practice of *Pranayama*. It brings about equanimity and helps to destroy past *Samskaras*. By its regular practice, one is able to control the sense organs and the mind. It has been said in *Vyasa Bhashya*:

तपो न परं प्राणायात् ततो विशुद्धर्मलानां दीप्तिश्चज्ञानस्य

"There is no greater *tapa* than *Pranayama*. It washes away the impurities and leads to the light of real knowledge".

Manu says:

दह्यन्ते ध्यायमानानां धातूनां हि यथा मलाः ।

तथेन्द्रियाणां दह्यन्ते दोषाः प्राणस्य निग्यहात् ॥

105

"Just as the impurities of metals (gold, etc.) are removed by the flame of fire, the *Indriyas* throw out their impurities through *Pranayama*."

In this context two couplets from *Rigveda* are worth knowing.

द्राविमौ वातौ वात आ सिंधोरापरावतः।
दक्षं ते अन्य आं वातु परान्यो वातु यद्रपः॥
आ वात वाहि भेषजं विवात वाहि यद्रपः।
त्वं हि विश्व-भेषजो दवानां इत ईयसे।

(Rigveda 10.137.2 & 3)

In our body two streams of breathing energies flow. They are *Pran* and *Apan*. The former flows from body cells to the heart, whereas the latter form heart to the atmosphere outside. The couplets, addressed to adept of *Pranayama*, tell him that *Pranvayu* brings strength, courage, energy for life and good health and that *Apanvayu* expels internal weakness & ill health from the body.

Prayer to *Pranvayu* is that it may bring in energy to cure diseases and to *Apanvayu* is that it may expel internal malfunctioning elements & various disease bearing weaknesses. Addressing the *Pran*-energy the prayer further says that, "thou are panecea for all diseases, and as messenger of Gods and cosmic energies you are blowing in side our system".

By these couplets sages have defined *Pran*-shakti as messenger of Gods and cosmic energies.

PANCHA PRANA

Although *Prana* is one, it has five sub-divisions on the basis of its location in the human bady. These are collectively called *Pancha Prana*.

1. **Prana:** This pervades the region from the throat to the heart. It helps in the dawnward flow to the breath.

106

2. **Apana:** It is located below the navel region. This *vayu* strengthens the large intestine and helps in the excretion of wastes like urine and stool.

3. **Samana:** It pervades the region between the heart and the navel and invigorates the digestive organs and controls the juices emanating from them.

4. **Udana:** The *Prana Vayu*, which pervades the region from the throat to the brain is called *Udana*. This *Udana Shakti* controls the organs above the throat, such as eyes, nose, ears, brain, etc. In its absence, the brain would not be able to function properly and we would lose our contact with the external world.

5. **Vyana:** This *Prana Shakti* pervades the entire human body. It coordinates *Prana Vayus* and other centres of energy in the body as well as controls and keeps in proper balance all the activities and movements of the body.

BANDHAS AND NADIS

We breathe through both the right and the left nostrils. This activity is performed through two separate channels in the nose. The flow of *Prana* through the left nostril is done by, what is known in yoga language, *Ida* or *Chandra Nadi*. This *Nadi* is supposed to be cool in effect. It influences the left part of the body and controls human thoughts. It has *Tamas Guna*. The flow of *Prana* through the right nostril is done by the *Pingala* or *Surya Nadi*. It provides heat and controls the right part of the body. It also regulates the *Prana Shakti* in the human body. It is supposed to have *Rajas Guna*.

Where the flow of *Prana* through these two *Nadis* meets in the body, *Sushumna Nadi* is supposed to exist there. This is the central canal. Neither hot nor cold, it controls and balances the other two *Nadis*. This subtle *Nadi* provides light and knowledge. Its main characteristic is *Sattva Guna*. It is also called *Saraswati* or *Shakti Nadi*.

One must understand that the objective of *Pranayama* is to effect the proper balance between *Ida* and *Pingala*

107

and to gain spiritual upliftment through the attainment of light and knowledge from the *Sushumna*. From physical point of view, a proper balance among the three *Nadis* provides health, strength, peace and longevity.

Bandhas

While doing *Pranayama*, certain *Bandhas* are also practised. They are three in number.

Jallandhar Bandha is performed by pressing the chin about three inches above the heart in the hollow formed in the neck.

Uddiyana Bandha is performed by exhaling the breath and by contracting the belly inwards.

The third *Bandha* called *Moola Bdndha* is performed by contracting the rectum upward.

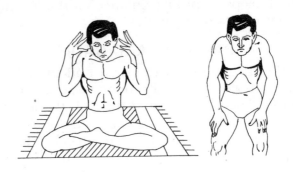

Jallandhar Bandha   *Uddiyana Bandha*

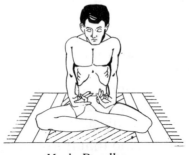

Moola Bandha

108

The Technique of Pranayama

1. **Place:** The first requisite of *Pranayama* is the selection of proper place for it. The place selected should be even, clean, peaceful and airy. It is better if *it is done in a garden. But the place which admits direct and strong wind should be avoided. Do not perform Pranayama* under a fan on full speed. A noisy or crowded place is also unfit for *Pranayama.*

2. **Time:** The most suitable time for *Pranayama* is the morning hours before the dawn when the atmosphere is clean and peaceful, free from dust and full of pure air. But the body must be properly cleansed before sitting for *Pranayama.* A beginner should practise for 5 to 10 minutes only. Gradually one can increase the time upto half an hour or even one hour. The duration should however be fixed according to one's convenience. But do not be irregular. Changing of duration every now and then and stopping the practice abruptly and then starting it all over again is not good; it can even be harmful.

3. **Posture:** The best posture for all types of *Pranayama* is *Padmasana* or *Siddhasana.* Sit comfortably in any of these postures, keeping the body erect but without any stiffness. Those desirous of doing *Pranayama* should prepare their body and mind by the observance of *Yamas, Niyamas* and by the exercise of asanas. In *Pranayama,* the body should stay erect without any movement of any limb; no part of the body should have any trace of tension. Both the hands should rest on the respective knees in *Jnan Mudra* and the eyes should be gently closed.

   Before starting *Pranayama,* the breath should be made normal in a natural way. Keep the body in a relaxed state and make the mind thought-free to attain full concentration.

4. **Technique:** *Pranayama* is not the way of normal breathing. It is a specific way of inhaling and exhaling. While doing *Pranayama* one should concentrate on one's breath; inhaling and exhaling should be slow and regular, *Pranayama* should be performed according to one's capacity and not in an uncontrolled and abnormal way. One should advance in it gradually in accordance with one's capacity and experience.

In doing certain *Pranayamas*, it is necessary to close the right and left nostrils. This should be done with the help of thumb and the third finger of the right hand. The first and the second fingers should be bent in such a way that they should touch the palm together. When it is necessary to close the left nostril, do so by putting on it the third finger. But when the right nostril is to be closed, thumb should be used. When it is desired to close both the nostrils, both the thumb and the third finger are to be used.

When the hands are not required for closing the nostrils, they should always rest on the knees.

There are three ways of controlling the breath in *Pranayama*: (i) *Pooraka* (filling the breath in), (ii) *Rechaka* (throwing the breath out) and (iii) *Kumbhaka* (holding the breath in or out). Holding the breath after filling it in is known as *Antrik Kumbhaka* and holding it after throwing it out is called *Bahya Kumbhaka*.

Some important instructions regarding Pranayama:

1. You can do *Pranayama* 3 to 4 hours after meals. The most suitable and useful time for *Pranayama* is the morning hours on an empty stomach.

2. Do not practice *Sheetali & Sheetakari Pranayama* in winter. Those suffering from gastric trouble also should not do this *Pranayama*.

3. Do not practice *Bhastrika* and *Surya Bhedan Pranayama* in summer.

4. *Nadi Shodhana* and *Bhramari Pranayama are very useful for uncertain and mentally retarded persons.*

5. *Deep breathing (inhaling and exhaling)* and *Antrik* as well as *Bahya Kumbhaka* are very beneficial for attaining longevity.

TYPES OF PRANAYAMA

There are about 50 types of *Pranayama* which are described in the *Shastras*. Here we describe only the nine important ones:

i.	*Kapalbhati*	ii.	*Agnisar*
iii.	*Bhastrika*	iv.	*Ujjayee*
v.	*Bhramari*	vi.	*Nadi Shodhana*
vii.	*Sheetali*	viii.	*Sheetakari*
ix.	*Surya Bhedan*		

Some of these like *Bhastrika* and *Surya Bhedan* are useful during winter, while some others like *Sheetali* and *Sheetakari* are specifically advantageous during summer. Others are good for all seasons.

Kapalbhati Pranayama

In *Kapalbhati*, *Rechaka* is done with full force. The attention of the practitioner should be fixed on *Rechaka* during the process. When the breath is exhaled with full force, the stomach should be squeezed inwards, so that the abdominal gas is thrown out with a jerk. In the *Pooraka* state, the belly regains its original position.

Technique: Sit comfortably in *Padmasana* or *Siddhasana* and normalise your breath. Try to throw your breath out through your nose with force. First do it slowly and then increase your speed. Do not make any effort to inhale. It is to be stressed that the breath has only to be thrown out and all effort should be directed towards that end. At the start, do it for 15 to 20 times. The practice can be increased to 50-60 times, but should be increased gradually. Also increase your practice according to your capacity. After doing the *Pranayama*, perform the three *Bandhas* (the *Moola Bandha*, the *Jallandhar Bandha* and the *Uddiyan Bandha*) for a few moments while doing

Bahya Kumbhaka. After that, remove the *Bandhas* and normalise your breath.

Kapalbhati increases the power of concentration by removing impurities from the nerves of the skull region. Those who sit in *Dhyana* should first do *Kapalbhati*. This helps to control the sense organs and keeps the mind at rest.

Agnisar Pranayama

Navel region is the centre of FIRE element, which is very essential for assimilation of consumed food. After the food is digested, the heat energy of this directs nutritive juices to all parts of the body.

In case of a malfunction in creation of heat energy, the digestive system cannot function properly resulting in various disorders like indigestion, acidity, gastric problems etc. It is therefore, very necessary to activate the energy centre regularly. Besides improving digestive system, *Agnisar Pranayama* fights obesity and improves blood circulation.

Method: Sit in lotus pose, placing hands on knees, shoulders stooped slightly forward and made rigid by gripping the knees, with body tilted forward a little bit. Exhale completely and pump the stomach till you can do comfortably. Relax the stomach and gently inhale. Repeat the exercise two or three time.

Special care must be taken to hold the breath outside upto one's capacity to do so.

Bhastrika Pranayama

Bhastrika is an important *Pranayama*. A large amount of *Prana Vayu* is supplied to the body by this *Pranayama* and at the same time impure air (carbon dioxide) is driven off the body and blood is purified.

Bhastrika means bellows. Its working is similar to that of the bellows of the blacksmith. Hence the name. *Ida*, *Pingala* and *Sushumna*, all the three *Nadis* are influenced by it.

Caution: Those suffering from high or low blood pressure and the ailments of the heart and the lungs should not do it. Healthy persons should generally do it.

Technique: Sit in *Padmasana* and make the body erect. Make the mind thought-free and relaxed. Now close the right nostril with your right thumb, inhale and exhale with full force. First do this slowly, then increase your speed and do it quickly for about 20 times. In the end, inhale fully, close the left nostril with your third finger, and perform all the three *Bandhas*. Increase the *Kumbhaka* according to your capacity. Now open the *Bandhas* slowly, lift the thumb from the right nostril and exhale through it slowly. Relax for a moment.

Repeat this process by closing the left nostril.

Now place your hands on your knees and do *Bhastrika* with both nostrils simultaneously. Do it slowly; increase your speed with practice.

It should be remembered that in this *Pranayama*, the rhythm in exhaling and inhaling should be maintained, and the time of inhaling should be equal to the time of exhaling. The *Pooraka* and *Rechaka*, both are done with full and equal force and no pressure is exerted on the openings of the nostrils in both the states.

Before doing *Bhastrika*, the practice in contracting and expanding the belly without moving any other limb is necessary. Such a practice brings efficiency in this *Pranayama*. *Bhastrika*, when done through the left nostril, influences the *Ida*; when done through the right nostril, it affects the *Pingala* and when done through both the nostrils, it influences the *Sushumna*. These are, respectively called *Chandrang Bhastrika, Suryang Bhastrika* and *Sampoornang Bhastrika*[1]. The first helps to control and purify one's thoughts, will power and emotions. The second helps in purifying and strengthening the *Prana* and manliness. The last, *Sampoornang Bhastrika*, helps to strengthen the central nervous system, the brain and intellect and the memory power.

113

By doing *Bhastrika* correctly, the *Prana* gets stability, the mind is brought under control, indolence is removed and *Dhyana* becomes easier.

Ujjayee Pranayama

The chief organs of respiration in the human body are the lungs. Before the air reaches the lungs, it passes through many organs. From the nose, the air enters the pharynx. This is also a very important organ of respiration. It is located in the neck behind the knot-like formation which appears to be protruding when viewed from outside. If we press this knot, breathing might stop leading to death. This also is the place where the *Vishuddhi Chakra* is located. The lower part of the pharynx is separated into two tubes. One of these tubes which is in front is the windpipe. From the pharynx, the air reaches the windpipe.

Whether we breathe through our nose or mouth, the breath reaches the lungs through this instrument. When this is contracted a little and we breathe, the sound of snoring is produced. In sleep, many people breathe the same way.

Technique: Sit in *Jnan Mudra*. First breathe 5-7 times normally, contracting this instrument a little. After a few days of practice, practise *Khechari Mudra* (It is formed by twisting the tongue inward and by touching the palate with it). Now inhale, producing the sound of snoring from the throat and exhale similarly. In the beginning, do it 15-20 times. Then gradually increase the number of such breaths. While removing the *Khechari Mudra*, swallow the saliva collected in the mouth.

In this *Pranayama*, the breath should go from the throat up to the heart, and vice versa. The speed of the breath should be slow and equal. The sound of inhaling and exhaling in this *Pranayama* should not be heard out.

This *Pranayama* is very useful in diseases like epilepsy and other ailments of the brain. Tonsils are removed and cold, cough, etc., are relieved. In fact, all the ailments of the throat, nose and ear are cured. The voice also becomes resonant. Those learning vocal music are greatly benefited from this *Pranayama.*

Bhramari Pranayama

The word 'Bhramari' is derived from Hindi 'Bhramari' which means bee. In this *Pranayama,* the buzzing sound of a *Bhramar* is produced while doing *Rechaka.*

Technique: Sit in *Jnan Mudra* and normalise your breath. Close both ears with your index fingers keeping the palms of the hands open and the elbows on level with the shoulders. Inhale slowly and fill your lungs with air. Now do *Antrik Kumbhaka* for a few seconds and exhale slowly producing the buzzing sound of a *Bhramar.* After this, do *Bahya Kumbhaka* for two seconds and repeat this activity. In this way, do it for five to seven times. Its frequency can be increased gradually. The rhythm of buzzing should not discontinue.

Bhramari Pranayama is in fact a spiritual exercise. By its long practice, one achieves the *Siddhi or Nad Bramha.*

In several physical disorders also it shows its effect. It helps relieve the tension of mind and keeps the mind alert. It also strengthens the veins and tissues of the brain and provides massage for them. It helps in the awakening of the *Ajna Chakra.*

Nadi Shodhana Pranayama

The purpose of *Pranayama* is to purify the nerves and thereby to strengthen the nervous system. It is as easy to do as it is useful. Increase its duration gradually after attaining the concentration of mind.

Sit in any comfortable posture: *Padmasana, Siddhasana* or *Sukhasana.* Make your breathing normal. Close your right nostril with your thumb and fill in the breath through the left nostril. When the breath has been filled inside, close the left nostril with your third finger and stay in this state of *Antrik Kumbhaka* for a few seconds.

Then lift the thumb from the right nostril and exhale slowly, keeping the left nostril closed.

Repeat the process by inhaling through the left nostril and exhaling through the right nostril. This will complete one full round of *Nadi Shodhana Pranayama*.

What needs to be emphasised in this process is the necessity of maintaining a ratio of rhythm in inhaling and exhaling. When you exhale after doing *Antrik Kumbhaka* (holding the breath in), your breath should not come out all at once in an uncontrolled way. Instead, it should be so regulated that it comes out very slowly and remains under your full control during this process. Hold your breath as long as you can conveniently do so; and when you release it, do it very slowly.

When you have enough practice of this process, set your breathing in a regular way. Suppose, you take 4 seconds in inhaling, then retain it inside for 8 seconds and release it also in 8 seconds. That is, the ratio of the three processes should be 1 : 2 : 2. After enough practice, change this ratio to 1 : 4 : 2. It means that if you now take 5 seconds in inhaling, then retain it for 20 seconds and release it in 10 seconds. You need not apply force for retaining your breath; it should be done in a natural way. There should be proper ratio between the *Pooraka Kumbhaka* and *Rechaka Kumbhaka*. While doing *Rechaka*, the breath should come out in such a slow measure that it is not felt at a distance of about 3 inches from the nose. Similarly in *Pooraka*, the inhaling should be so slow as if only air around a distance of about 3 inches is affected.

Pooraka and *Rechaka* are technical terms used in *Pranayama*. In yoga, taking in and taking out breath is called *Shwasa* and *Prashwasa*. *Pooraka* and *Rechaka* are not simple *Shwasa* and *Prashwasa* but something more. In *Pooraka* the lungs are filled with air in measured and rhythmic way in a very slow process. Similarly in *Rechaka* lungs are emptied of air in a regular, rhythmic and measured way.

116

When we hold our breath in *Antrik Kumbhaka*, we expand our lungs and fill pure air in them. The pure air is therefore able to reach each and every cell. The cells of the lungs get purified and strengthened in this way. When we do *Bahya Kumbhaka*, on the other hand, we retain the breath out. The cells of the lungs therefore contract and the impure air is squeezed out of them. This dual process makes the entire body clean, pure and light. This also increases longevity.

In simple breathing, we generally take the air in and then exhale it immediately thereafter. The pure air is therefore not fully utilized in the body. But *Kumbhaka* is the unique process which brings about its full utilization in the body. The importance of *Kumbhaka* is beyond words. It is common knowledge that when we want to do some work with all our force, such as lifting a heavy load-discus throw, etc., we usually hold our breath. It is therefore obvious that we can increase the strength and capacity of our body by *Kumbhaka*.

In fact, *Kumbhaka* is not difficult to perform because it only requires one to hold one's breath. But this does not mean that we should start doing it in an abnormal way. This can be risky or even dangerous. Increasing the period of *Kumbhaka* abruptly without sufficient prior exercise or doing it in an irregular and casual way can do more harm than good. It is therefore very essential that we should progress gradually and increase its practice by slow measures, so that we do not come to harm.

Nadi Shodhana Pranayama is an excellent *Pranayama*. It is very beneficial in the ailments of the nervous system, lungs and hypertension. In this *Pranayama* the centre of concentration should be *Anahata Chakra* (see next chapter for the description of *Chakras*).

Caution: Those suffering from high or low blood pressure should not do *Kumbhaka* in this *Pranayama*. They can however practise *Pooraka* and *Rechaka* slowly.

Kumbhaka should be done only after the disease has been completely cured, and then too in small measures.

Sheetali Pranayama

This *Pranayama* has a cooling effect on the body and mind. It is very effective in relieving the heat of summer days. It is also good in ailments like high blood pressure and the diseases of the skin. It helps to purify blood. It relieves the feeling of thirst and is specially useful for hot-tempered people who fly into a rage at the slightest provocation.

Technique: Sit in a relaxed manner in the state of *Jnan Mudra*. Bring your tongue out, turn its edges and give it the shape of a drain. Do *Rechaka* and then inhale deeply with effort through the tongue drain. Do *Antrik Kumbhaka* and perform all the three *Bandhas*. First open the *Uddiyan Bandha*, the *Jallandhar Bandha* and after that *Mool Bandha*, and exhale through the nose slowly. In this way, do it for eight to ten times, concentrating on the *Vishuddhi Chakra*.

Sheetakari Pranayama

Its effects are similar to those of the *Sheetali Pranayama*. It relieves heat and has a cooling effect on the body and the mind.

Technique: Sit in *Padmasana* or *Siddhasana*. Fix with force the front part of your tongue at the roots of your teeth and touch the palate with its tip. Now lock your teeth and jaws fixing firmly one upon the other and inhale through the sides of the mouth, producing a sizzling sound. Do *Antrik Kumbhaka* and use all the three *Bandhas*, as in *Sheetali Pranayama*. Increase the duration of the *Antrik Kumbhaka* gradually. Do it eight to ten times.

Surya Bhedan Pranayama

This is a *Pranayama* as well as a technique of arousing the *Kundalini Shakti*. *Surya Bhedan* aims at piercing and arousing the *Pingala Nadi*. This arouses that part of the brain which is the source of *Purusha Shakti*. In other words, this *Pranayama* arouses and increases the latent powers of a person. It provides heat to the body and purifies blood. Its regular practice increases the red corpuscles in the blood significantly, and provides relief in the dreadful disease of leprosy. It invigorates the mind and increases will power.

Technique: Sit in *Padmasana*. Place the first two fingers of your right hand on the middle of the eyebrow and close the left nostril with the third finger. Inhale deeply and quickly through your right nostril. Now close the right nostril also with your thumb and do *Antrik Kumbhaka*. Perform all the three *Bandhas* also. Open the *Bandhas* one by one: first *Uddiyan*, then *Jallandhar* and lastly *Mool Bandha*. Now throw the breath out slowly during this *Pranayama*. Do it five times. Try to increase the duration of the *Antrik Kumbhaka*: first do it for half a minute, then increase to 2-3 minutes. The centre of *Dhyana* in this *Pranayama* should be *Manipooraka Chakra* i.e., *Nabhi Chakra*.

It is not necessary to practise all types of *Pranayama* described above everyday. It is very important that *Pranayama* should be done under the guidance of an expert in this field, because a wrong step can mean more harm than good. Excessive practice beyond one's capacity can also be very harmful. The golden rule is to do it according to your capacity. Also, choose the right *Pranayama* suitable for you and increase your practice very gradually. Generally, the practice of *Nadi Shodhana* and *Ujjayee* for 10-15 minutes daily is sufficient for a normal man. *Kapalbhati*, *Bhastrika* and *Sheetali* are usually done according to the season.

❏❑

8. Dhyana

It is the mind of man which chains him to the world or leads him to *Moksha* (liberation). Man is not only a living being made of bones, flesh and blood. He also has a mind endowed with various types of *Samskaras*. Right from his childhood whatever he sees, learns, experiences or imagines, is turned into *Samskaras*. His unfulfilled desires, his joys of success, his sorrows and memories of all types remain buried in the depths of his mind and it is they which contribute mostly towards the formation of his *Samskaras*.

Desires are born in the mind. The fulfilment of one desire leads us to the pursuance of several others. But the desires are unlimited. Therefore, the fulfilment of all of them is impossible. The unfulfilment of desires or their suppression is the root cause of all sorrows and tensions.

Mind is just like an unbridled horse. It roams about everywhere and does not easily submit to any control or discipline. It is active all the time with movements as swift as they are uncontrollable. By its very nature, it does not fix on any object for a long time. This fleeting movement of the mind dissipates its energy. If one takes a decision, the mind will coin so many excuses to counteract it. Suppose one decides to join a yoga class the next morning, the mind will do its best to defeat this idea by several excuses, e.g., why not enjoy the morning sleep when the weather is pleasant and air is so cool. If these suggestions fail, the mind would give another excuse, i.e., today the bowels are not properly clean, so it would not be possible to have full advantage of the asanas; therefore, why not start from tomorrow. And this tomorrow never comes, because the mind will try to break the will power of a person by one way or the other. One who falls prey to the mischievous designs of the mind can never stick to one's decisions, because if one gives in once, one is lost forever. Next time, the mind will offer more powerful arguments against one's decision. On the other hand, if these arguments of the mind are rejected in the first instance, it will weaken its hold.

The joys and sorrows of the world are caused by the mind. The likes and dislikes depend upon the mind of man, because it is the mind which projects them as good or bad, lovable or detestable. The senses see, hear, smell, taste and touch the outward objects and convey their sensations to the mind. It is the mind that enjoys them. In yoga, therefore, the first means are the senses, thereafter comes the mind. The victory of the mind by the mind is yoga.

There are several means by which a *Sadhaka* tries to control the mind; *japa*, *tapa*, *yajna*, *karma* and *jnana* are some of them. But the best of all these is *Dhyana*. It is however to be remembered that control over mind cannot be achieved so easily. It is not possible to achieve success in this field just in a few days. Constant practice, detachment of the mind from its sense objects and firm determination can however gradually lead one to the path of success. In this process, the key lies in *Dhyana*. As the *Dhyana* grows and matures, the mind goes on becoming more and more pure; its folds open up; the old *Samskaras* are dissolved, and the mind becomes free from impurities. One then progresses from the unconscious to subconscious state, from subconscious to conscious state, and from conscious to superconscious state, i.e., the state of *Samadhi*.

In general also, *Dhyana* saves the mind from dissipation and takes it to the realms of peace and perfection. The concentration of mind is increased, its fickleness and instability are removed; it rests in stability, so that its energies are increased. *Dhyana*, thus, awakens the slumbering energies of the mind.

Dhyana is essential for all. Ascetics, *grihasthis* (family men), students, doctors, lawyers, shopkeepers, men and women, all are benefited by the practice of *Dhyana*. It is as useful for patients as it is for healthy men. Even if it is not perfect, *Dhyana* is a must for at least five minutes daily for everybody.

Some Prerequisites of Dhyana

1. The place for *Dhyana* must be clean, airy and free from all types of disturbances. It is better if it is practised at one particular place everyday.

2. The best time for *Dhyana* is *Brahma-Muhurta*, i.e., the time between two-and-a-half hours before sunrise till sunrise.

3. *Dhyana* is also beneficial if practised before going to bed at night. One should practise it for a few minutes at night after washing one's hands, feet and face. This ensures peaceful and sound sleep.

4. While practising *Dhyana*, one should sit in a comfortable posture, e.g., *Padmasana*, *Siddhasana* or *Sukhasana*. If it is practised within four hours after taking meals, one should better sit in *Vajrasana*. Always sit erect, so that the hind of the head, the neck and the spine should form a straight line. There should be no tension in the mind. The eyes should be closed with hands resting on the knees in *Jnan Mudra*.

5. The body should remain stable in *Dhyana* just like a rock; but there should be no stresses and strains. All body movements should remain suspended while practising it.

6. But the most essential factor of *Dhyana* is meticulous regularity. It should be practised daily without any break whatsoever.

Some Means of Dhyana

1. **Asanas:** While doing asanas, concentrate fully on those parts of the body which are stretched and

influenced during a particular asana. This will increase your power of concentration. Asanas are the easy means of achieving concentration of mind. They impart not only physical vigour, but increase mental power also.

2. **Pranayama:** Mind and *Prana* are deeply interrelated. There are two main causes of the instability of the mind: attachment and *Prana* (breath). Victory over one of these leads to the victory over the other. When the mind is connected with breathing, it sees the breath coming out and going in. It then gets concentrated on the process of breathing. Ultimately, it merges with the breath. All its waverings are then stopped, its fickleness disappears and it achieves a perfect state of stability. *Pranayama* is therefore the best and the easiest method of controlling the mind.

3. **Thought Observation:** Sit in *Dhyana*. Let the thoughts come in your mind. Do not force any thought to come nor prevent or suppress any. Be a spectator and observe your thought process. See how your mind wanders from one thought to another, from one incident to another, from past memories to future plans. You have just to observe all this as if you are someone different from your mind, a separate entity or an outside observer. After a few day's practice, you will find that as soon as you start this process, the thought process of the mind slows down, stops wandering and it begins to be more stable.

4. **Thought Creation:** Sit in *Dhyana*. Bring some thought or idea into your mind. Fix your mind on it for five to seven seconds and then remove this idea from your mind altogether. Bring another thought, concentrate on it for five to seven seconds and then remove it. Repeat this process several times. Now stop all thoughts for a few seconds as if the mind is resting or it is on holiday. Keep it free from all

123

thoughts for a few seconds. In this way, practise *Dhyana* for 10 to 12 minutes daily. After a few days' practice, you will have a better control on your mind. Thought creation is an effective method of mind control.

5. **Thought Removal:** Let any thought come into your mind. Then remove it. Let another thought come; remove this also. In the same way, go on removing the thoughts which naturally come into your mind. You have however not to force the thoughts to come nor have you to prevent them from coming. You have only to remove them. Whatever thoughts come, they are not to be allowed to stay; remove them. After 10-12 days' practice, you will find your mind stable, peaceful and free from disturbance.

6. **Trataka:** Fixing unflinching sight on an object is *Trataka*. Sit in a comfortable posture. Place the picture of your deity before your eyes at a distance of about one metre, or place a white sheet of paper with a black or green circular mark. Eyes may otherwise be fixed on the tip of your nose. Watch any of the above objects without blinking your eyes till you get tears in them. Then close your eyes gently. Practise this several times for about ten minutes.*Trataka* not only cures several eye diseases it also helps in achieving greater concentration of mind.

7. **Dhwani Yoga:** Practise *Dhwani Yoga* (see Page 63) several times. Perform with rhythm and melodiously. Listen to your sound with full attention. This can be done by silently pronouncing 'OM' and listening to it. By this practice, the mind gets absorbed in the sound and thus attains concentration.

8. **Ajapa-Jap:** Recite a *mantra* in your mind without producing any sound. Then correlate the *mantra* with your breath, binding the mind and the breath in one chain. For example when reciting OM (ओ३म्)

124

inhale with ओं and exhale with म्. Similarly in सोम्, inhale with सो and exhale with हम्; and in ओ३म् नमः शिवाय, inhale with ओ३म् नमः and exhale with शिवाय. You should completely concentrate on the breath and the *mantra*. When breath gets stabilised, mind will also get stabilised. When in grip of anger or disturbing thoughts, practise *Ajapa-Jap*. All your tension will disappear in a few minutes. This is one of the easiest ways of calming the turbulent mind.

9. **Attention on Chakras:** Seven subtle *Chakras* have been presumed by yoga in our body. Out of these, five are in the spine, one in the forehead in the centre of the eyebrows and the seventh at the back of the head at *Brahmarandhra*. In Tantra Yoga, the detailed characteristics of each *Chakra* have been given. These *Chakras* are located in the subtle body at important nerve centres. Concentration on these *Chakras* leads to the purification of the nerves and nerve fibres. Purification achieved through this process helps the body and the mind to grow in peace, and remove tension.

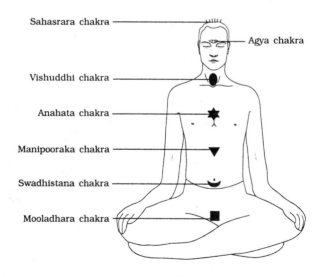

Chakras

125

Schematic Diagram of Brain, Spinal Cord and Autonomic Plexuses

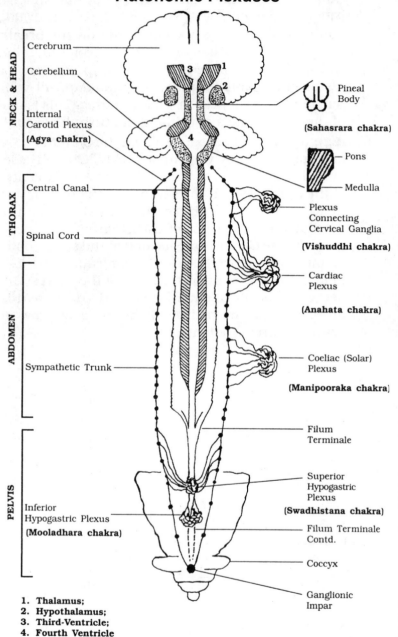

NECK & HEAD

Cerebrum

Cerebellum

Internal
Carotid Plexus
(Agya chakra)

THORAX

Central Canal

Spinal Cord

ABDOMEN

Sympathetic Trunk

PELVIS

Inferior
Hypogastric Plexus
(Mooladhara chakra)

3 1
2

4

Pineal
Body

(Sahasrara chakra)

Pons

Medulla

Plexus
Connecting
Cervical Ganglia

(Vishuddhi chakra)

Cardiac
Plexus

(Anahata chakra)

Coeliac (Solar)
Plexus

(Manipooraka chakra)

Filum
Terminale

Superior
Hypogastric
Plexus

(Swadhistana chakra)

Filum Terminale
Contd.

Coccyx

Ganglionic
Impar

1. **Thalamus;**
2. **Hypothalamus;**
3. **Third-Ventricle;**
4. **Fourth Ventricle**

126

1. **Mooladhara Chakra** is supposed to be in the region of the coccyx (bone ending spinal column), slightly above the rectum.

2. **Swadhishtana Chakra** is supposed to be in the sacral region and occupies the area of five lower vertebrae of the spine.

3. **Manipooraka Chakra** occupies next five vertebrae from below after the first five occupied by the Swadhistana Chakra. It is thus located in the lumbar region, as may be seen in the figure given. From the front it is near the navel.

4. **Anahata Chakra** is in the upper spine and is also near the heart. It is supposed to occupy twelve of the vertebrae.

5. **Vishuddhi Chakra** is in the neck and occupies the remaining seven vertebrae of the vertebral column.

6. **Agya Chakra** is located in the centre of the two eyebrows. This also is the place of the divine light and the 'third eye'. Sadhakas sometimes begin their sadhana by concentrating at this important point.

7. **Sahasrara Chakra** is at the back of the head at Brahmarandhra. This is the highest of all the subtle Chakras and is reached in the highest state of sadhana.

The literal meaning of 'chakra' is wheel. In Tantra Yoga, the *chakras* are represented usually by lotuses of different number of petals. While the lowest *chakra* (i.e., *Mooladhara*) is represented by a lotus of four petals the highest one (i.e., *Sahasrara*) is represented, as is obvious from its name, by a lotus of one thousand petals.

The *chakras* are connected with each other by *Nadis* or nerve channels which go along the spinal column. As has been mentioned earlier also, there are three subtle nerve channels or *Nadis* which run along the entire vertebral column. On the left of the spine is *Ida*, on the right is *Pingala* and in the centre *Sushumna*. These nerve channels cross each other at certain nerve centres. In fact these very nerve centres are called *chakras* in Tantra Yoga.

Kundalini Yoga also recognises these subtle *Chakras* and *Nadis*. Kundalini is supposed to be in the shape of a white serpent lying coiled up one and-a-half circle in its house at the base of the spine. Kundalini, when awakened or aroused, releases tremendous energy as in the case of an earthquake or a volcano, It is usually awakened by a prolonged and sustained practice of *Pranayama* and Hatha Yoga. After its awakening, the *Sadhaka* sometimes undergoes tremendous suffering. In modern times also, a few great souls have achieved success in awakening their Kundalini, Pandit Gopi Krishna* being the most famous among them. According to him, the awakening of the *Kundalini Shakti* is beset with great dangers. It can even lead to madness or death if the *Sadhaka* is not blessed and guided by the *guru* or the Almighty. Ultimately it leads to the highest state of bliss. But bliss is achieved neither so quickly nor so easily. The Kundalini awakens from the base of the spine and rises up the subtle *Nadis*, pierces the subtle *Chakras* one by one and finally reaches *Sahasrara Chakra*, the seventh and the highest *Chakra* representing a thousand-petal lotus. When the Kundalini reaches this *Chakra*, the soul is engulfed in soft, divine light and internal peace is achieved. This is the final goal or the destination. It is the superconscious state or *samadhi*. When a soul merges or unites with the divine light in this way, real or true 'yoga' (union) is said to have been achieved. All forms of yoga are directed towards this end.

One of the striking features of yoga is that all types of people can benefit from it. Persons having very diverse natures and with different mental set-up can choose the *Chakra* suitable for them, each according to his own state of mind. Persons with unstable and restless mind should concentrate on *Mooladhara Chakra* to get quick success. After achieving the stability and peace of mind, one should

Kundalini, Orient Paperbacks, 1976

128

start concentrating on the other *Chakras*. Those who are endowed with stable mind and *Sattvic* nature should begin their practice from *Anahata Chakra*. When their *Dhyana* achieves complete maturity, they should then concentrate on *Vishuddhi Chakra* and *Ajna Chakra*.

The food of the mind are the objects of the senses. When we concentrate on *Chakras*, the mind gets absorbed in their form, size and colour, etc. It then fixes the senses also on them. The mind comes to possess the toy of the *Chakras* and gets busy with them. When however it gets bored with this play, it is easy to make it look inward.

10. **A Remarkable practice:** Sit in a comfortable posture and concentrate on breathing. Look at the outgoing and incoming breath. Fix your mind on the breathing process. Then pronounce 'OM' slowly in a deep tone eleven times. Again sound 'OM' within your mind five times, so that the sound resounds inside and does not come out; the attention remaining on the sound of 'OM'. Then repeat the *mantra* by mixing it with the flow of breath, keeping the attention on the centre of the eyebrows. From this place, take your attention on your deity and have his *darshana* in your mind. Now make the mind free from all thoughts for one minute, so that it becomes completely empty. Treat the mind as if it is resting, as a person without work on a holiday. Bring the mind again to its full consciousness, take the attention to your deity and then to the centre of the eyebrows, and then to the *mantra*. Recite 'OM' two times in your mind, and then practise *Dhwani Yoga* five times. Shift your attention back to breathing process and with this bring this remarkable *Sadhana* to an end.

Benefits of Dhyana

Every practitioner of *Dhyana* is benefited from its practice. It is a remarkably useful practice for those who get worried or agitated easily or those who suffer from insomnia and lack of self-confidence. Swami Vivekananda has likened mind to a drunken monkey which is stung by a scorpion and is visited by a ghost. Mind by its very nature is shifting and unstable. But when it gets drunk with the wine of lust, is stung by the scorpion of jealousy and is visited by the ghost of ego, then its control is well nigh impossible. But the practice of *Pratyahara*, *Dharana* and *Dhyana* leads it to stability, peace and concentration. We then no longer remain the slave of the mind; rather mind becomes our obedient servant. This is the way to peace and growth.

❑❑

9. Exercises of the Eyes

The eyes are a very important part of our body. *Neti &* *Trataka* are very useful for improving eyesight. Daily practice of these *Kriyas* is a must. These two *Kriyas* are mentioned in detail in chapter of yogic purification practices.

Besides yogasanas, there are certain exercises for the eyes which keep the eyes healthy and save them from many diseases. By toning up the connecting muscles and nerves of the eyes, they even improve the eyesight. Some of these simple exercises are explained here, which can be performed after doing yogasanas. Sit in *Padmasana*, *Sukhasana* or *Siddhasana*, keeping your head, neck and spine straight, and perform the following exercises:

1. **Vertical Movement:**
   First look upward towards the middle of your forehead and then on the tip of your nose without moving your head. Only the pupils of your eyes should have upward and downward movement. Do it quickly for 24 times and then close your eyes gently for five seconds to provide rest.

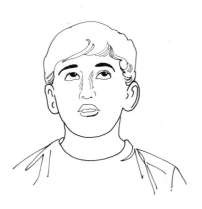

Vertical Movement

2. **Horizontal Movement:** Spread your hands sideways. Close your fists and raise your thumbs. Now first look towards your right thumb, without moving your neck, then towards left thumb. Repeat this exercise 24 times and then close your eyes gently for five seconds.

131

3. **Diagonal Movement:** First look above the corner of the right eye and then towards the ground near left knee. Do this 12 times. Similarly, look above the corner of your left eye and then bring attention on the ground near your right knee. Repeat this also 12 times. After this, close your eyes gently for 5 seconds and give the eyes the rest they need.

Diagonal Movement

4. **R e c t a n g u l a r Movement:** Make an imaginary rectangle before your eyes. Make it as big as you can. Then move your eyes on the four corners of the rectangle from left to right 12 times, from right to left also 12 times. Close the eyes gently after this for about five seconds.

Rectangular Movement

5. **Circular Movement:** Make an imaginary circle from the earth to the sky and move your eyeballs first clockwise for 12 times and then anti-clockwise 12 times. Give rest to the eyes.

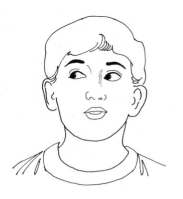

Circular Movement

6. **Forward-Backward Movement:** Sretch your right hand forward. Raise your thumb, closing the fist with the fingers. Fix your gaze at a point beyond your thumb and slowly bring it closer and fix it ultimately on the thumb. Do that for at least 10 times. Now gradually start bringing the thumb closer to the eyes and repeat the process of looking beyond the thumb and at the thumb. Go on doing it until the thumb comes very close to the eyes. Close the eyes gently and give rest. This exercise improves the eyesight.

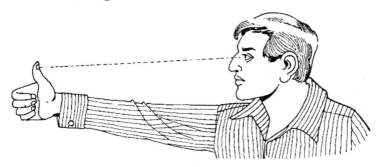

Forward-Backward Movement

At the end of these exercises close your eyes gently. Now rub your palms with each other and place them on your eyes. Do it three times. Open your eyes and look at a green plant or grass.

Note: All the above exercises can be done in a standing posture. Regular practice of the above exercises removes tension and exhaustion. They lend lustre and brightness to the eyes and as a result the eyes become healthy and beautiful. These exercises are to be done after doing Asanas.

Some Important Steps for the Care of the Eyes

Besides, the above exercises, the following practices are also very useful for the proper care of the eyes.

1. **Palming:** This is an easy and quick method of providing relief to the tired eyes. Sit comfortably in a chair or on the ground. Close the eyes gently. Bend the palms in the shape of a cup and place

them on your eyes, the right palm on the right eye and the left palm on the left eye.

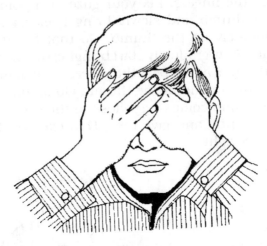

Palming

The palms should not touch the eyes, but only cover them completely. The fingers should rest on the forehead, and the nose should remain uncovered. Let your elbows rest on your knees.

Whenever you feel that your eyes are tired due to continuous reading or overwork, practise palming for ten to fifteen minutes. You will find that your eyes become fresh after this.

2. **Blinking:** This is another easy, quick and natural method of giving rest to the eyes. Blinking, i.e., raising and dropping eye-lashes quickly can be done during any type of work. Gazing or staring is the chief cause of damage to the eyesight. Dropping the eye-lashes is essential at least once if not twice in ten seconds. Blinking also helps during reading. It saves the eyes from getting tired and one can read for a long time at a stretch. Book-worms must cultivate the habit of blinking.

3. **Washing Eyes with Cold Water:** Cool, pure water works as a tonic for the eyes. Whenever you wash

your face, do not forget to splash water on your eyes from a distance of about 10 cm. Do it for twenty times. This will refresh your eyes and provide new vitality to them.

4. **Providing Sunlight to the Eyes:** Sunlight, if provided in a proper way to the eyes, is extremely useful for them. But direct sunlight on the open eyes is not only harmful but dangerous also. There are several ways of feeding the eyes on sunlight. Some of these are described below.

a. Close your eyes and stand facing towards the sun. Now move your neck towards right and left for five to seven minutes, to let the sunlight fall on all parts of the eyes. This exercise is particularly useful if done in the morning when the sun is not very hot.

b. See the sun through water. The light of the sun coming through water is very useful for improving the eye sight. The old Hindu custom of *Argha* (giving water to the sun) with raised hands has probably this secret behind it.

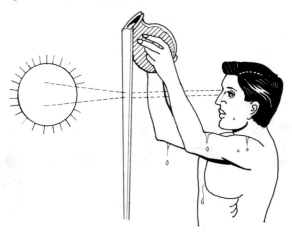

See the sun through water

c. See the sun through green leaves. Take two green leaves of *Pipal* and bring them close to your eyes.

135

Now look at the sun through the leaves. This practice also provides energy to the eyes.

5. **Washing the Eyes with Triphala Water:** Soak Triphala in water at night and wash your eyes with it in the morning. This has a very good effect on the eyes. You can also use eye washer cups, specially made for washing the eyes. Washing eyes with simple clean water is also very useful if done twice a day in the morning and evening with the help of washer cups. These inexpensive cups are available with the Bharatiya Yoga Sansthan.

Swinging Exercises

We describe here two very important exercises which have been found most practical and useful in improving and restoring normal eyesight. Some western books have also described them as most useful.

Swinging Exercise No. 1

Stand erect, keeping your feet about 30 cm apart. Now move your entire body to and fro like the pendulum of a clock. Take care not to raise your feet off the ground completely; only the heels of the right and left feet should be raised turn by turn and not the toes and the fingers. The second important point to remember is that the entire body should move, and not only the waist or the body above the waist. The movement of the body should be from head to foot and in a harmonious way.

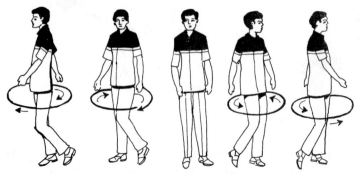

Swinging Exercises

Do this exercise for about six minutes. Close the eyes for a few seconds or a minute if you so desire. You can close and open your eyes alternately. This exercise has a very good effect on the eyes. It is in fact a very good exercise for toning up the entire nervous system.

Swinging Exercise No. 2

This is similar to the above exercise and has similar effects.

Stand erect, keeping your feet about 15 cm apart. Raise the heel of your left foot, and turn your body right by 90º. Keep the head, arms and eyes so relaxed that they should also rotate with the rotation of the body. Now raise the heel of your right foot and move your body 90º towards left in such a way that you return to the original position in which you were at first. Similarly, raise your right heel and return to your original position.

To sum up, you have first to turn left by 90° and then to right by 90°. Then you have to return to the same position. You have never to make an about turn. The entire exercise should be done slowly without giving jerks to the body. This may be done for approximately five minutes.

❑❑

10. Yogic Massage

Ever since our births, the massage plays an important role in developing our body and in helping us to adjust to our physical environment. Consciously or unconsciously everyone uses it to beneficial effects. Soon after the infant's birth, his massage starts. The mother pats and cuddles the body, the physical touch that helps him to grow well fast. Wealthy massage also imparts strength to the bones, and relaxes the muscles. Every living being, including bird or animal, adopts the basic principle of massage and keeps itself fit. No doctor teaches this. It's a natural instinct.

Just as regular practice of yogasanas and good food habits are essential for good health, the massage also plays a vital role in this respect. It helps improve the functioning of veins and arteries and makes them healthy. The muscles gain elasticity. On the whole massage helps to improve the general health, prolonging the life.

It also plays a vital role transporting food stuff from one part of the body to the other, for thin people it works miracles. If a person doesn't eat for several days but gets himself massaged by an expert he can survive for several days. His body would use less energy, as massage will supply him with diet.

Main Advantages of Massage

1. The circulatory system gets activated and helps body organs function efficiently.

2. Proper circulation of blood helps to cleanse the body of the impurities collected at different points in the body through outlets like breath, sweat, stool and urine.

3. The excretory organs like skin, rectum, lungs, kidneys etc., get strengthened and they start working more efficiently.

4. The digestive organs like liver, small intestines get activated and function more smoothly.

138

5. Massage helps to reduce fat.
6. Patient suffering from ailments like rheumatism, paralysis, polio, tuberculosis, headache and muscular problems get relief with massage.
7. The pores of skin improve.
8. The veins and arteries gain elasticity and body becomes more efficient and oily.
9. In case of chronic diseases the skin loses its vitality. The massage helps the skin to regain the lost vigour.
10. Those who do not do exercise or patients who cannot exercise can find in massage an ideal substitute. Because like exercise the massage improves the blood circulation and cleanses the body of impurities.

TYPES OF MASSAGE

Massage can be of many types:

1. Oil massage 2. Dry massage 3. Foot massage 4. Cold massage 5. Warm-Cold massage 6. Powder massage 7. Electric massage.

For every massage there is certain procedure which must be followed faithfully. Different ailments call for different massage, and they must be done keeping the patient's conditions in mind. Not all patients can be given the same type of massage.

The cold massage is ideal for patients suffering from insomnia, dry scratching, excessive heat, nervous weakness, burning sensation and vibration in hands and legs. Even light massage with oil proves useful in these cases.

For weak and thin people oil massage is ideal.

Dry massage and cold massages are good for reducing fat.

Those suffering from paralysis, rheumatism, backache, pain in legs, polio, sciatica greatly benefit from oil massage, foot massage, hot-cold massage and electric massage. During fast one should have oil massage.

Dry massage, powder massage and oil massage help to relax the body.

A normally healthy person benefits from oil massage and cold massage.

Apart from these in many ailments massage of some particular parts of the body produces incredible results. For instance massage of the back and backbone in case of weakness of nerves; massage of neck, head and backbone in case of insomnia; the massage of front part of neck in case of tonsils; chest and back in case of asthma and bronchitis; head and neck in case of headache, leg and lower part of the back in sciatica; back and stomach in anemia and particularly massage of liver is very beneficial for the patients.

Oil Massage: The oil massage should be done in the direction of heart. Although one can massage oneself, is better to get somebody else to do massage. Leave your hand lose and massage toward the heart from the upper parts of the body downwards and from below upwards. The Massage should begin from leg, knee, thighs, arms, stomach, chest, back neck and head. The massage activates the veins and helps to cleanse the body of impurities. The massage should concentrate on the muscles and not on the bones. This will help the muscles to become elastic and flexible.

Other Types of Massage are: Tapping, rubbing, kneading, patting, wringing, rapping, swapping, thumping, pressing, punching and heating with hand.

Daily Massage: Massage the body well for five to seven minutes before the bath. This can be an oil massage or simply dry one by rubbing the hand on the entire body.

Leg: Rub a little oil on the leg. Start from the ankle and using circular motion bring the hand up. Use the palms of both hands and rub in opposite directions. Pat and strike gently the leg with hands.

Arm: Rub oil on the arm and massage upwards starting from the wrist. Use circular motion. Pat and strike gently with hand.

Stomach: Rub oil with both hands on stomach from right to left using clockwise motion. Then catch the flesh with fingers and rub downwards upwards. This helps to reduce fat. Now press with fingers and rub many times towards right and move upwards using clockwise motion.

Chest: Rub the chest all over with oil from left to right, and down to up. Move the hand outwards from the middle. This will broaden the chest. Cup both palms and gently tap the chest all over. This will benefit the heart and lungs.

Back: You can't massage your own back yourself, so, as far as you can expand your hand, gently press and rub outwards. However, if you can get someone else to massage for you, it would be better. Rub oil at the back and massage well from left to right and down to up. Place both palms side by side with back bone in the middle, press and rub downwards. Press with thumbs on both sides of the backbone and rub upwards. Rub every vertebra properly. Gently pull the flesh from different places and massage. Cup the palms and pat gently.

Neck and Face: Using circular motion massage all over the face and gradually move the hand downwards from the chin and rub the neck. Massage the face downwards. Use fingers to massage around the eyes. Without pressing hard use palms to massage clockwise.

Head: Put oil on the head and massage right upto the roots of the hair. Use circular motion to massage forehead and head. At the back of the head move hands downwards. Cup the palm and pat the head. Do this massage daily for ten minutes before the bath. Give massage more times on holidays.

❑❑

11. Physical and Mental Health: Some Practical Hints

A regular daily routine disciplines the body and the mind. Without this discipline, one cannot get full advantage of the yogasanas and other yogic practices. Regularity and discipline are a must for the practitioner of yoga or the *Sadhaka*. Yogasanas, if done irregularly and without proper preparation, do not lend their full benefit to the body and the mind. So, we must have an ideal daily routine.

Sound Physical Health

Early Rising: This is the first and the foremost requisite for a *Sadhaka*. Early to sleep and early to rise is a maxim no where more appropriate as here. Sleeping early brings sound sleep, makes the mind calm and the thoughts pure. Early rising removes laziness and brings agility in the body and the mind. An early riser is able to finish with his daily chores like walking, exercise and cleaning bowels without undue haste. After getting up early, one should clean one's teeth, wash one's face, drink a glass of water and should go to answer the call of nature. One should go for evacuation at the fixed time everyday. Even if the feeling is not there, one must still go to latrine at the fixed time. Those who develop this regular habit never suffer from constipation. The children in the family should also be taught to go to latrine at a fixed time everyday. Cleaning one's bowels is the most essential process of cleaning. No amount of outward cleanliness can be of any help if the bowels are not clean. If the natural process does not help, the next course is enema, because enema is helpful in cleaning the bowels. The very first condition of good-health is the daily cleaning of the bowels regularly as well as punctually. This will make your body light and increase your appetite.

Cleanliness of the Teeth: Most people clean their teeth in the morning only, and that too with a tooth-paste and brush.

One must, of course clean one's teeth in the morning; but cleaning them before going to bed is most essential, because food particles left in the teeth rot in the mouth during the night and spoil our teeth and gums. The ideal way is to clean the teeth with a neem twig (datun) in the morning and with a toothpaste and brush at night. One must learn the proper method of brushing one's teeth; improper brushing can do more harm than good. The children should also be encouraged to develop the habit of brushing their teeth before going to bed. Scratching them with a pin or a hair pin can be very injurious. Chewing provides exercise to the teeth. Therefore, one must chew one's food properly.

Bathing: It is also very essential to take bath daily with fresh water. Our skin provides an outlet to the internal impurities of our body. It is of utmost importance to keep the skin clean and pores of the skin open, so that the passage for the removal of impurities remains open and clean. Bathing is also an art. Throwing a few mugs of water on the body is not bathing. Before bathing, one should rub or massage one's body gently, to produce heat. While bathing, the body should be rubbed thoroughly. It is not essential to use soap daily. After the bath, the body must be dried properly with a towel. Some people wear clothes on wet body, which is not proper. It is better to dry one's body in the sun after cleaning it with a towel. It would be much better if the body is warmed also in the sun before bathing.

One must always take bath with fresh water. Hot water bath makes the skin weak. It is also not so refreshing as compared to fresh water. If the fresh water is not available from a pump or a well or if it is severe winter, then one should heat the water to bring it to the temperature of the atmosphere. It is also not advisable to bathe with icy cold water. The advantage of bathing with fresh water is that it helps to bring the blood circulation up to the skin. It therefore imparts activeness and freshness to the body and the mind.

Clothes: Clothes should be simple and comfortable. In a hot country like ours, loose clothes are more suitable than tight ones. Tight clothes obstruct the free movement of limbs; they also obstruct free movement of blood in the body. It is good to wear thick clothes of *khaddar* during summer to save oneself from *loo*. In the rainy season, the lesser the clothes on the body, the better, otherwise thin, fine clothes are ideal to help the body keep cool. Warm clothes are necessary in winter so that the body does not lose its heat.

The polyester clothes are harmful for the body. Specially the clothes which are worn next to the skin like the vest. If you wear polyester shirt, the vest under it should be of cotton.

Sleep: Sound sleep is the sign of good health. Sleep helps repair the body organs and overcome wear and tear of the body. It also helps to remove the impurities of the body so that when we get up next morning, we again become fresh and ready for work. Waking and working late at night or spending the better part of the night in cinemas or clubs is harmful for health.

The children below five should be allowed to sleep as long as they can. For a young man, eight hours sleep is enough. But with the increase of age, sleeping hours are automatically reduced. A person above 50 should not sleep beyond six hours. Even four hours' sleep, provided it is sound and is taken in the first half of the night, can be sufficient in some cases. Body health depends on the degree of soundness of our sleep. An interrupted half-waking sleep cannot keep us healthy and happy in life. For sound sleep, the following points are useful:

1. The place of sleeping should be clean and airy. Windows and ventilators should be open to let in fresh air.
2. The bed should be hard, but comfortable. In the winters the blanket etc., should be large enough to enable one to have sound sleep, which gives new energy and one gets up completely fresh in the morning.
3. The cot should be tight. Sleeping on a *takhat* or hard bed is preferable so that the spine remains straight and the blood circulation is not hindered in any way.
4. Do not sleep with the face covered. Breathing should be through the nose, so that the air is filtered before it enters the windpipe; air is also warmed by breathing through the nose. It is a bad habit to breathe through the mouth.
5. It is better to eat one's supper three to four hours before going to bed. Mind should also be free from all

worries at the time of going to bed. If there is some amusement before sleeping, it provides relaxation to the tense muscles and nerves. The sleep in that case is sound and refreshing.

6. It is a good habit to wash one's face and feet before going to bed. After this, sit in *Vajrasana* on the bed itself and concentrate on your deity or do your prayers, or perform *Mantra Japa*, if you have any. Deep breathing for a few minutes also ensures sound sleep.

7. Urinating before going to bed makes the bladder light. Light massage of eye muscles or even head helps bring relaxation. Do not wear tight clothes while sleeping. The clothes should be minimum and loose. A glass of cold water before sleeping is also good. The pillow should not be too high.

Good Behaviour: Yoga has no meaning, if there is no perceptible change in the social behaviour of the *Sadhaka*. A yoga practitioner always thinks well of others. He is not greedy or selfish. He leads a balanced life without causing, even without desiring to cause, harm to anybody. He is sweet to others. He is a *Sadhaka* and leaves no chance in his life of serving others. All this brings him nearer his goal—union with Almighty, i.e., yoga.

Yoga and Mental Health

Our body is made up of innumerable living cells and each such cell, according to yoga, contains another subtle cell which controls the biological cell. According to the modern science, our blood consists of more than 75,000,000,000 healthy cells, which float in it and carry the oxygen to all parts of the body to nourish them. These same cells take the nourishment from the blood and provide it to all the organs and tissues, infuse our digestive system, keep the heart-beat regular, heal up the wounds and stop bleeding. These cells perform all these functions automatically. Yoga believes that these cells can perform all such functions because each cell is "intellectually developed" to some extent. In spite of this intellectual development of these cells, the human mind exercises control over them. They therefore obey the orders of the conscious as well as the sub-conscious mind. Thus, the body is in a natural way under the influence of mind. It is therefore easy to infer from this that for the health and proper growth of the body, a healthy mental attitude and sound mental health are essential.

In *Ashtang Yoga*, mental growth through *Pratyahara* and *Sadhana* has been emphasised upon. The body is therefore under the control and direction of the mind. Human mind has been divided into three categories depending upon its qualities or *gunas*.

Sattvic Mind: A *Sattvic* mind is completely at peace and cool like the moon on the full moon night. Its chief characteristics are kindness, truth, contentment, love, devotion, humility and happiness. In this state, the blood pressure remains normal and the living cells multiply and become stronger. They obey the orders of the mind without any hindrance. The person endowed with this type of mind can control and develop his body at will.

Rajasic Mind: In this state, the *Sattvic* traits of the mind are overshadowed by the cleverness of the intellect. The mind then gropes in the darkness of worry, sorrow, jealousy, greed, anger, fear and luxury. In such a state, blood circulation becomes abnormally rapid and leads to turmoil and confusion in the body. The cells are also in a disorganised and disturbed state. Their growth and development is stopped and their deterioration and weakness begins. Any amount of exercise and diet cannot then save the body from disintegration. Body health is therefore bound to suffer.

Tamasic Mind: When we start feeding ourselves on the poison of two deceit, theft, ignorance, laziness, violence, adultery and other sinful activities, then our attitude towards life also gets distorted. We start taking pleasure in all these debased activities. Our thinking is completely blurred, because our blood circulation is so disorganised that the cells stop their normal functions. They start getting filled with poison instead of life. None can save such a person from his doom.

It is now obvious how mind can influence the body. Mental health is the first condition not only for the growth and development of the mind, but also for the body. It is therefore all the more necessary to acquire *Sattvic* mental traits through constant effort. In fact, physical and mental health are inseparable. One cannot be improved at the expense of the

146

other. If the mind is sick, it will not allow the living cells to grow and become strong. And if the body is sick it will make the mind helpless, because it cannot control and direct body functions.

All elements of nature are in constant motion, i.e., their atoms are vibrating all the time. The entire universe is therefore being spun by a powerful source of energy. This vibrant motion is well organised and well regulated. We may not be able to see this motion, but its existence cannot be denied. Life itself cannot exist and grow without this source of energy. Every element of the universe vibrates vigorously or slowly according to its own individual characteristics. Nature is also in constant vibration; heat and temperature are the other forms of energy like motion. All are in fact the manifestations of the energy which pervades every atom of the universe.

This energy which provides motion to objects and brings about changes in the universe is termed as *Prana* in Sanskrit. *Prana* (vital energy) and *Akasha* (matter) are all pervading. Modern science says that these two basic elements of the universe cannot be destroyed; their quantity therefore cannot be increased or decreased. The concept of yoga is a little different from this. According to the yoga philosophy, they are not indestructible in themselves; they are the manifestations of God. And since God is neither born nor destroyed, they also are endowed with these properties, i.e., they are indestructible by virtue of His indestructibility. Science considers *Akasha* (matter) and *Prana* (energy) as two different things. But according to yoga, physical matter or *Akasha* is the gross form of energy or *Prana*. Similarly, *Prana* is the gross form of mind, which itself is one of the smallest parts of omniscient God and manifests His qualities.

So, the only thing above the mind is God, while *Prana* is under the mind and physical matter is under *Prana*. Thus, except God, nothing is above or more powerful than the mind, whereas *Prana* and physical matter are under it. Raja Yoga emphasises the control, training and *Sadhana* of the mind, because it believes that if the mind is within control, then no other yoga practice is necessary. Each and every object of the world, whether organic or inorganic, is made up of atoms. Matter is the manifest form of these atoms. The subtle form of matter is energy or *Prana* and the subtle form of *Prana* is mind. But mind is the gross form of God Himself. It is also believed, both by yoga philosophers and scientists that the macro or gross form of an object is always under the control of its micro or subtle form. That is, physical matter is ruled over by *Prana* and *Prana* in turn is controlled by the mind. Thus, what is called *Pranayama* in yoga language is actually the art or rather the science of controlling *Prana* by the mind or will power. If the mind is able to control *Prana*, then the gross forms of *Prana* (i.e., physical objects) will automatically come under the control of the mind. That is why *Pranayama* has been laid so much emphasis upon in Hath Yoga and its importance has been recognised and established in yogic postures and *mudras Pranayama* forms a very important part of *Ashtang Yoga* of Patanjali also. But whether one does *Pranayama* or *Yogasanas*, one can have full benefit out of these activities only when one constantly tries to purify the mind and make it *Sattvic*. Mind, *Prana* and body (or physical matter) are the three different states of the same thing—atom. So, any *Sadhana* without the training of the mind is incomplete.

❏❏

12. Yogic Diet and Fasting

A ll living beings on this earth need food. Most of them eat a particular type of food, just as a horse eats grass and grain, and a lion eats raw meat. These species intuitively know what they should eat. But paradoxically, man, although the most intelligent of them, usually does not eat what he needs. While other species eat only a few varieties of food, man eats innumerable types of cooked and uncooked foods. Another strange fact commonly observed is that man, in spite of all his knowledge, does not eat his food well. That is why man is the sickest of all species today. He has established thousands of hospitals to cure sickness and disease. He has set up large factories to manufacture drugs and medicines. The medical science has made enormous progress in the 20th century. But man is still the sickest of all species on this earth. Why? Let's try to find, if there is any relationship between our food habits and our sickness.

The Functions of Food

We need food to live. We cannot live without food beyond a short period. Food is therefore necessary for all living beings. Food performs the following four functions:

(a) **Growth:** Food is essential for growth. Without food a living organism will stop growing. The living cells in our body multiply after getting nourishment from the food we eat. Insufficient or a wrong type of food does not help healthy growth.

(b) **Repair:** Living organisms sometimes damage their parts by accident. Constant work also causes wear and tear of the body parts. If we get a wound or cut, it heals up after some time. If we damage our skin due to some burn etc., it regains its shape in due course. The body needs food for all these functions.

(c) **Energy:** We spend our energy when we do work. That is why after doing considerable work, we get tired. We then need food and rest to regain the lost energy. If

149

we do not get food, we would become weak.

(d) **Protection from Diseases:** We need to protect our body from diseases and keep it healthy. For this, we need vitamins and mineral salts in our food. Vitamins neither provide energy nor do they repair or replace the worn-out parts. But they are essential for our proper health.

So, we need food which can give us all the ingredients required by our body. We also need sufficient food—neither more nor less. That is to say, we should eat the right amount of food containing the right amount of nutrients.

Balanced Diet

Different foods contain different amounts of elements needed by our body for the above four functions. These vital elements are called nutrients. So, the diet which contains all these essential nutrients in right quantity will be balanced diet for us. The essential nutrients required by our body are: carbohydrates, proteins, fats, minerals and vitamins.

Carbohydrates and fats mainly provide energy to our body. Wheat, rice, potato, banana, etc. are very rich in carbohydrates. Jaggery or sugar is another source of carbohydrates. Ghee, butter, oils, cream and milk are full of fats.

Proteins help the body to grow. They also help it to replace the dead or worn-out parts and to repair the damaged parts. Children need more proteins because their bodies have to grow rapidly. Pulses, milk, cheese, curd, egg, fish and meat are rich in proteins.

Vitamins and minerals are present in milk, cheese, fruits, vegetables and meat etc. Vitamins keep our eyes, bones, gums, etc. healthy. Minerals like phosphorus and calcium are necessary for the formation of healthy bones and teeth, while iron compounds are required for the formation of red blood cells.

There is no single item of food which can provide us with all the necessary nutrients (although fresh milk) contains most of these. It is therefore essential to eat a combination of foods to get all the necessary substances required by our body. The quantity of these ingredients required by each body is not the same. So we must select our food items according to the needs of our body. Generally, a person doing a lot of physical work will need more of fats and carbohydrates to recoup the energy lost by him in excessive physical work. A child needs more proteins than an old man, because the child's body needs more protein for growth. A sick person may be deficient in some substances, but he may not need carbohydrates and fats.

So, a balanced diet is one which is suitable in all respects, sufficient in food value as well as adequate in quality and quantity according to the needs of a body. To keep our body healthy and fit, we must follow the 'balanced diet' principle. Our ancient medical system of Ayurveda also emphasises this principle of balanced diet.

विनापि भेषजैव्याधि पथ्यादेव निवर्त्तते।
न तु पथ्यविहीनस्य भेषजानां शतैरपि॥

"No medicines are required by a person who correctly follows the prescribed diet scheme. But one who does not follow this principle of diet cannot be helped even by hundreds of medicines."

We should therefore know what to eat and follow the diet scheme as far as possible. Children should also be given their diet according to this principle. In fact, everyone should follow the diet system properly.

Restraint in Eating

It is not enough to select our food items judiciously. We should also know how much to eat and how to eat. Our food does not change into energy immediately after reaching our stomach. It has to undergo several complicated processes before it is turned into useable form and is assimilated in our system. Food is first chewed and broken into smaller pieces by our teeth; the salivary glands in the mouth at the same time mix saliva with the food. In the stomach, it is churned and its contents are thoroughly mixed. Here also many glands mix digestive juices with the food, so that the food undergoes several chemical changes by the help of enzymes and acids formed in this process. Similarly, food is subjected to further chemical changes by the action of the pancreas and liver, which secrete several enzymes and juices to react on it. Ultimately, it is absorbed by the small intestine.

So, we must understand that digestion is a complicated process in which all our digestive organs take part and our glands secrete digestive juices. Therefore we should not eat such foods which require overwork for our digestive organs. Nor should we eat more than the required quantity. When the organs are required to do work endlessly without any rest, they ultimately become weak, with the result that some of them are unable to work properly. This causes sickness. It would be better not to tax our organs to the extent of getting them damaged. So, we must exercise restraint in eating. We must also provide rest to our digestive organs occasionally, so that they remain effective and in perfect working conditions all our life. This can be done by observing occasional fasts. Apart from the diet tables so diligently prepared by dieticians, we have this simple but *golden rule of diet control*:

पूरयेत अश्नेन अर्धं तृतीयं उदकेनतु ।
वायो: संचरणार्थाय चतुर्थं अवशेषयेत् ॥

"One should fill half the stomach with food and leave one-fourth for water and one-fourth for the movement of air".

We can ourselves feel and know how much to eat. It is simply a bad habit to eat one's fill; one must still feel hungry after eating one's meal.

Our Food Habits

One of the major causes of illness is wrong food habits. Even the best food eaten in a wrong way can cause disorders of the body. So, we must know what to eat and how to eat.

(i) **Fried vs Natural Food:** We usually spoil our food-stuffs before eating them. We have come to like fried food. In frying the food not only loses its vitamins and other essential nutrients, but it also becomes hard to digest. We consume too much of carbohydrates when we eat a lot of wheat, rice, potatoes, sugar, etc. Usually green leafy vegetables, fruits and other raw foods are missing from our diet. Raw or boiled vegetables should be an essential part of our daily diet. For those suffering from constipation, these are a must. Not only they provide necessary vitamins and salts, but also ruffage which prevents constipation. Vegetables like tomato, carrot, cucumber, cabbage, onion, salad, ginger and raddish can be eaten raw. Other vegetables, when cooked, should never be fried. They should be first washed, then cut in big chunks and cooked in steam or boiled. Butter or cream can be added only after boiling or steaming the vegetables.

We should therefore change our habit of eating fried food. If we regularly eat boiled vegetable, we are sure to develop a taste for them. Sooner it is started, the better.

The best and most ideal food, however, is "natural food". By natural food we mean the food which Mother Nature offers us. Nuts, fruits, vegetables, pulses and cereals can be eaten without putting them on fire. While fruits, nuts and vegetables can be eaten without any further processing, cereals and pulses can first be sprouted and then eaten raw.

(ii) **Drinking Water with Food:** We usually drink water with or immediately after our meals. This is a wrong habit. Actually, there is no need to take water at the time of taking our meals. But we feel its need because we do not chew our food properly. There are some among us who seem to have no time for eating; they therefore do not chew their food, they swallow it. They do not allow the digestive saliva of the mouth to mix with their food. So they throw their food down their throat with a lot of water.

Water does not help in digestion; it actually hinders the process of digestion. Moreover, because of the pressure of water the intestines are not able to absorb all the digested food and it passes off the intestines. Water should be taken half an hour before or one hour after the meals. We should drink water several times between our lunch and supper Water washes our intestines and rids them of all impurities. We are therefore saved from many intestinal troubles. Water is actually a great purifier and we should make full use of this property of water. There are many yogic purifying practices in which water is used for cleaning the stomach or the intestines. These have been described in Chapter on "Six Types of Yogic Purification Practices". An early morning dose of water checks bile, imparts vitality to all our organs and helps keep bowels clean. Lemon juice and a spoonful of honey, can also be mixed with it according to one's liking and taste.

(iii) **Appetite Loss and Non-stop Eating:** Many of us have no fixed time for eating. Some of us eat all the day. But the worst of all, we eat when we are not hungry, and thus harm our digestive organs. In the opinion of medical as well as yoga experts eating when not hungry is a heinous crime against oneself. If we are committing this crime, we must be ready for the punishment also. No amount of drugs can save us from the resultant damage to our system. We may not feel the intensity of the damage done to our organs in our young age, because our organs have a wonderful capacity to bear excesses on them. But the corroding process is set and the system is strained and weakened by overwork. Moreover, when we eat without hunger the digestive juice do not mix with our food in full quantity. This results in indigestion and several other disorders. Our organs need rest also, as all of us need rest to recoup our energy and be ready for work again. So, a few hours' rest to our digestive organs is necessary not only during the night but also during the day. It is therefore better to take only two full meals in 24 hours instead of three or four.

Some people are of the opinion that breakfast, when we are rushing for work in the morning, is not essential. Breakfast, they say, is hungerless eating. We eat because we have made a habit to eat at this time. So, the golden rule is to eat when one is hungry. This will not only make us receptive to food, but our mind and all our organs will concentrate on eating and digesting food. This will ensure good digestion and full utilization of the food eaten.

Every one of us must try to follow this old maxim: we should eat to satisfy our hunger and not our palate. But this is easier said than done. This is, in fact, one of the most difficult things to do.

If one is able to control one's palate, one can control probably everything else. So, the control of palate is the first step towards *Sadhana*. It is also the biggest achievement towards self-discipline.

We should always eat in a clean, quiet and peaceful atmosphere. Eating hurriedly in a fit of anger or in the grip of anxiety and fear is not desirable. Eating by the roadside is a common practice. It should be avoided as far as possible, because the food eaten from a roadside shop is usually full of dirt and dust and may have been prepared in unhygienic conditions.

Some of us eat to please others. It is good to please others. But it is not good to go on eating to please others. One can understand taking one or two morsels if someone insists. But eating a full meal on a full stomach is very harmful.

(iv) **Sugar vs Jaggery (gur):** White, mill-made sugar has now become our daily diet. We take it in milk, tea, coffee, *sherbat* and other sweet preparations. We should however know that taking excess of sugar means inducting excessive quantity of uric acid in our body system. This generally results in such dangerous diseases as diabetes, rheumatism, acidity and pyorrhea. In children, it causes worms. With the increase in the consumption of sugar there has also been an increase in the number of patients of these diseases. If we analyse sugar as a food, we will find that it has no food value. All its nutrients are actually destroyed in the process of crystallisation. *Gur* and *shakkar* however retain their protein, fat, vitamins, iron, calcium and other mineral salts. *Gur* is slightly laxative also. It helps the children to get relieved from thread worms.

But the type of jaggery that is available in the market is usually unhygienically prepared and stored. The system of manufacturing and storing must improve before people can be attracted towards this important food item. Sugar is more acceptable to people because it is cleaned properly and is stored in bags. But jaggery is usually very clumsily packed and stored. This enables the flies to get in. We must do something to improve this system.

In any case, we should reduce the quantity of sugar in our diet, if it cannot be eliminated altogether. Those who can do it should replace it by honey, dates and other natural sweeteners. Honey, in fact, is a food as well as a tonic. As a food, it is full of nutrients like dextrose, formic acid, iron and many enzymes. Moreover it is most easily digestible. As a tonic, it is a heart stimulant and brain tonic. On the other hand, unwashed dates are unhygienic. So, it is essential to wash them before eating or before using them in sweet dishes.

(v) **Tea and Coffee:** As *gur* has been replaced by sugar in our diet, so have milk, curd and *lassi* been replaced by tea and coffee. Most of us drink 4 to 8 cups of tea or coffee daily. But tea and coffee are not among the essential nutrients. In fact, they have no food value, i.e., they do not provide any substance essentially needed by our body. If we take them out of our diet, no harm would be done. Many people have however become tea or coffee addicts. Moreover, it has now become a fashion or a social custom to offer tea or coffee to guests. But we should also be aware of the evil effects of excessive consumption of tea or coffee. Medical experts issue warnings to the people from time to time against the excessive use of these drinks. It would be better to restrict the number of cups to the minimum if we are unable to stop tea and coffee altogether. Tea is more harmful when tea leaves are boiled. So, at least stop boiling tea leaves if you cannot stop it altogether.

(vi) **Tobacco and Liquor:** They have no place in the food of a person. Moreover, they are not at all conducive to the yogic way of life. So, they have not been discussed here.

Yogic Diet

Yoga is an ancient science. It has all along insisted on a nourishing but non-stimulant, vegetarian diet. Yogic diet satisfies three main conditions: (i) it is nourishing, i.e., it provides all the essential nutrients to the body, (ii) it is vegetarian, (iii) it is pure and non-stimulant. According to medical science, if a food satisfies the condition No. (i), then it is fit for consumption. But yoga, being a subtle science, makes subtle distinctions. Proper food is the first requisite of a *Sadhaka*. So says Lord Krishna in the *Bhagvad Gita*.

युक्ताहारविहारस्य युक्तचेष्टस्य कर्मसु।

युक्तस्वप्नावबोधस्य योगो भवति दुःखहा॥

"Yoga becomes the destroyer of woes and can be accomplished only by him who is regulated and moderate in diet and recreation, regulated in performing actions, and regulated in sleeping and waking."

So, one who wants to advance on the path of yoga should first pay attention to his diet. There is no conflict between yoga and modern science as far as the principle of balanced diet is concerned. But yoga diet would exclude all those food items which are non-vegetarian and intoxicating, because according to yoga, food is not for physical fitness alone; it also affects mental and spiritual state of a being. So, yogic diet, apart from giving physical fitness, is conducive to mental and spiritual upliftment. It is simple, natural and *Sattvic*, besides being nourishing. In fact, yoga lays emphasis on *Sattvic* food.

The *Bhagvad Gita*, which is the most exhaustive treatise on yoga, divides food into three categories on the basis of its effect on the human mind: *Sattvic*, *Rajasic* and *Tamasic*. *Sattvic* food is the best and the most superior type of food. The medium type of food for worldly man is *Rajasic* food and the most inferior type of food is *Tamasic* one. Our ancient scriptures proclaim in one voice that the type of food determines the type of man. It is to repeat the oft-repeated maxim: "As the food, so the mind, as the mind, so the man."

Lord Krishna has explained the three types of food to Arjuna in the *Bhagvad Gita* in the following three *shalokas*:

आयुः सत्त्वबलारोग्य सुखप्रीतिर्विवर्धनाः।

रस्याः स्निग्धाः स्थिराहृद्या आहाराः सात्त्विकप्रियाः॥

कट्वम्ललवणात्युष्ण तीक्ष्ण रूक्ष विदाहिनः।

आहाराः राजस्स्येष्टा दुःखशोकामयप्रदाः॥

157

यातयामं गतरसं पूर्ति पर्युषितं च यत्।
उच्छिष्टमपि चामेध्यं भोजनं तामसप्रियम्॥

"Foods which promote longevity, intelligence, health, happiness and delight and which are sweet, bland, nourishing and agreeable, are dear to the *Sattvic* type of men.

"Foods which are bitter, sour, saline, excessively hot and cold, pungent, dry, burning and giving rise to pain, grief and illness are dear to the *Rajasic* type of men.

"Food which is half-cooked, insipid, putrid, stale and polluted and also impure is dear to the *Tamasic* type of men."

A man chooses his food according to his taste and nature; those endowed with *Sattvic* nature choose the *Sattvic* food, those with *Rajasic* and *Tamasic* natures choose the *Rajasic* and *Tamasic* food respectively. Conversely, the type of food liked by a person ultimately determines and forms his nature.

Sattvic food accordingly provides ideal nourishment, promotes vigour and vitality. Alongwith high physical endurance and longevity, it imparts mental and spiritual balance to the consumer of this type of food. For these reasons, *Sattvic* food generates pious and pure thoughts. Not only does the body retain its natural vigour for a full life of hundred years, but the mind of *Sattvic* person is capable of rising to great spiritual heights. Both the body and the mind of a person feeding on *Sattvic* food ward off senile decay and disease. *Sattvic* food is pure and vegetarian.

Rajasic food, however, combines both vegetarian and non-vegetarian dishes. We are given to fried, over-cooked, highly oiled and spiced foods. These foods are rich in food nutrients and contain concentrated food items including sweets, ghee, fried vegetables, butter, cheese, meat, eggs, fish etc. They are more suited for fighters, warriors etc., who need animal strength. Their use, moreover, should be restricted to young age when human organs are strong enough to digest them. But ultimately, these foods lead to the weakening of the body and the mind and premature death.

Tamasic food is the lowest grade food. It is unwholesome, stale, unbalanced and decomposed and causes irritating poison in the blood. This type of food is harmful for the body as well as the mind.

Ideal Yogic Food-stuffs

After discussing all aspects and all types of food, it can easily be concluded that the following types of food items can be included in the yogic diet, which not only help the body to remain strong and active but lead one to high mental and spiritual attainments:

(1) All nuts and fruits, (2) all kinds of vegetables and edible green leaves, (3) all kinds of pulses, (4) milk, curd, butter-milk, (5) dates; honey and jaggery, (6) wheat, rice etc., (7) sprouted pulses and cereals.

The Need and Importance of Fasting

Many ancient scriptures highlight the importance of observing fasts on days and periods of religious importance. The Hindus, the Muslims and the Christians therefore observe fasts on grounds of religion. Fasting is a sort of *Tapa*, a method of self purification. So, almost all religions of the world emphasise the importance of fasting as a means of individual purity. It is presumed that the control on the sense of taste is the first step towards self-discipline and self-realization. Hot blood, it is said, creates lust, bad temper, greed, jealousy, etc. in man. Fasting has a cooling effect on the blood (not, of course, in the physical sense). That is why, those who observe fasts are usually calm, quiet, balanced and religious minded. During the period of fasting, the mind loses much of its turbulence and submits to discipline. *Tapa*, meditation and concentration (*dhyana*), etc., are much more easy during fasting than when one's belly is full. That is why probably in Sanskrit the word 'Upavasa' has been used for abstaining from food. Its literal meaning is "to stay near", i.e., to stay near God or to reside in His realm. Man does go near Him during fasting partly because of *tapa* or self-purification, and partly because of single minded concentration of mind. It is therefore not difficult to understand why all the religions of the world have laid so much emphasis on fasting.

Fasting is equally important as a curative and recuperative means. During the process of digestion, all digestive organs have to work for the digestion of the food taken. The glands have also to keep on secreting digestive juices to help in the process of digestion. In fasting, all the digestive organs, i.e., the stomach, the pancreas, the liver, and the small and large intestines get much needed rest. We all know the value of rest, which is a tonic for the exhausted and weary organs. Just as after sleep and rest we feel more strong, fresh and energetic, so is the case with internal organs also. They also need rest as we do. Rest improves their working and lends them strength and vitality. And on their efficient working depends our health.

In fasting, the blood in our body solely devotes itself to the task of destroying germs and other poisonous wastes in our body, because the work of digestion is held in suspense. The body therefore gets more healing power during fasting than it normally possesses. The vital healing power within our body thereby becomes more active. Therefore fasting sometimes does wonders in curing chronic disease, the cure of which eludes all other means of treatment. Thousands of experiments performed by naturopaths all over the world confirm the belief that fasting has a curative effect. When all other methods of curing a disease have failed, fasting may be given a chance.

But long fasts are better undertaken under the advice of an expert naturopath. One or two-day fasts can be safely undertaken without any expert medical guidance by *Sadhakas* as well as householders, and by the patients and healthy persons all alike.

The Technique and Principles of Fasting

There are no very hard-and-fast rules as to when to fast. Some people observe fast for a day once a month; others do not observe any particular system and undertake a fast when their system needs cleansing. The following points may be useful for observing a fast:

1. Do not eat any food during the day of fasting. Drink as much as clean water as you can when you feel thirsty. Water cleans the entire system and washes away the impurities which might have accumulated in the system from time to time.

2. If in the beginning you find it difficult to observe complete fast for one full day, you can begin with a partial fast. Do not take anything during the day except water. In the evening, take fruit juice or fruits, or fruit

and milk. That is to say, take no solid food except fruits.

3. Those who cannot observe even a partial fast, may drink orange or some other juice thrice a day. Vegetable juice can also be taken in the absence of fruit juice.

4. It is essential to cleanse your bowels in the morning. It is better to take an enema of simple water, after the normal motion to cleanse the bowels thoroughly. Your fast will do you good when you start it with clean bowels.

5. Fast should always be broken with a glass of fruit juice. In the absence of fruit juice, you can take fruits which are pulpy and easily digestible, e.g., orange, pappaya, grapes, apple, etc.

   It is a bad practice to break the fast with a solid, hard or fried food like *prantha, puri*, sweatmeats, etc. In fact, it does more harm than good. It will be good to eat easily digestible food for two to three days after the day of the fast.

6. One should take as much rest as one can during the fast. Hard physical labour should be avoided during the time of the fast. Those whose nature of work is such that they have to do hard physical labour, they should observe only partial fast. Those who can observe silence during the fast should do so to save energy.

7. Long fasts of more than two days should be undertaken under the guidance and advice of an expert naturopath. It is however not essential to consult a doctor when one resorts to fasting to cure indigestion caused due to careless eating. In small ailments like headaches, stomach aches, bad cold, one may safely go in for a fast.

8. Fasting increases our will power. We should exert our will power fully on the day of the fast and should control our mind's wanderings. The purification of the body and the mind achieved during fasting enables us to bring our mind to one-pointedness and fix it in meditation. It is easy to meditate on the day of fasting because fasting makes the mind quiet, placid and thus easy to control. ❏❏

13. Principles of Yoga Therapy

I t would be difficult to find too many people who never had any sickness in their life. In fact, the number of people who are "really healthy" in today's world would be very insignificant. Most of us are however sustaining our life somehow by consuming huge quantities of drugs. Ironically, even so-called healthy people are also consumers of drugs and tonics to build and maintain good health. We have become so drug conscious, thanks to the huge publicity by the drug manufacturers that even at the slightest headache we gulp a number of tablets to get quick relief.

We have many systems of medicine in our country, but the allopathic system is the most predominant among all these. It is also the most commonly practised system in the world. It has many antibiotics like penicillin, terramycin, streptomycin, chloromycetin, sulpha drugs, etc., used to kill bacteria or germs which attack us and cause diseases of several kinds. But as they kill germs of a disease inside our body, they also destroy some vital tissues and red blood corpuscles because they are potent poisons. They can sometimes kill a patient instantly instead of saving him. But most of them do cause what are called "side-effects," i.e., while they kill a certain type of bacteria, they at the same time weaken or damage some of our delicate internal organs.

Main Features of Yoga Therapy

The world is actually suffering from over-drugging. Can man escape drugs? Yoga can prove to be a great saviour of mankind if its practice is popularised in the length and breadth of the world, because yoga has the capacity to keep the body free from most types of sickness and thus to make the unnecessary use of drugs. It is easy to find thousands of allopathic doctors themselves who have lost faith in allopathic drugs. Yoga not only advises to avoid drugs but it also helps an individual to get rid of drugs. Another plus point of yoga is that it operates not only on the physical level but also on

162

the mental and spiritual planes. So far as the malfunctioning of glands is concerned, no medical system has really achieved any breakthrough. Here also, it is yoga which can restore the normal functioning of glands by corrective yogic practices. At the same time it is the best preventive system, the regular practitioner of which can escape the agony of illness. This system comprises three types of activities or exercises: the *yogasanas*, the *mudras* and the *pranayama*. While the *yogasanas* invigorate our internal organs, the *mudras* ensure healthy functioning of the glands and the *pranayama*, besides purifying our blood, soothens our nervous system. So, this trinity of yoga system is capable of restoring and ensuring normal health for us without the necessity of drugs.

Diet Control

Yoga will help more when we have diet control also. If we dump all sorts of poisons in our stomach, yoga will not be able to clear that debris like a magic wand. It is a scientific system based upon the minute and deep knowledge of human physiology. It can therefore operate effectively if we take balanced and controlled diet, the principles of which have been discussed earlier. Yoga as a curative is therefore firmly linked with diet control. We know that in any system of treatment, the medical expert also prescribes the diet for the patient. But in yoga, strict observance of diet system prescribed is most essential. So, while describing common diseases and their method of cure through yoga practices, we must lay full emphasis on diet control. Some very common diseases and yogasanas that help cure them are given below for the benefit of readers. But in acute cases, personal guidance of an expert is very essential. Moreover, it is beyond the scope of this book to give exhaustive knowledge of all diseases.

So, we have only mentioned the name of the *yogasanas* against the diseases in which they are useful. Complete yoga therapy is the subject of a complete book or a yoga hospital.

Start with Clean Stomach

But before the above-mentioned list is given, it is considered most essential to point out that *yogasanas*, *mudras* and *pranayama* should always be performed on empty stomach and clean body, preferably after taking bath. Yoga is for purification of body, mind and spirit. So, one must start with clean body and clean mind. Clean bowels is actually the very first and the most essential condition of yogic practices. Those who do not have their bowels clean in a natural way should therefore first perform those exercises which help in this. *Bastikriya* described in Chapter on "Six Types of Yogic Purification Practices" is prescribed by ancient *acharyas* for complete evacuation. But experience shows that common people cannot and do not practise such yogic *kriyas* because they are difficult to perform. Naturopathy has helped solve this problem by enema. But yogic method is better because it is more natural. Realising the difficulty of performing *Bastikriya*, a simpler practice of easy evacuation has been devised which is as effective as original *Bastikriya*. The following paragraph describes this useful practice, which can be performed by the sick as well as healthy people. It is very beneficial practice for constipated patients also.

Easy Method of Evacuation: Drink two glassfuls of water after brushing your teeth in the morning. Those who suffer from constipation may mix the juice of a lemon and a little salt with water. Lie flat on your back and raise your legs slowly up to an angle of 30^0. Stay in this position for one or two minutes and then raise your legs up to 90^0 and stay in this position also for a minute or two. After this, raise your lower body up further by giving support of your hands at the back below the hips. In this position, your body should be a perpendicular to the ground. Stay in this position from 2 to 3 minutes. Those who cannot raise their legs and stand in this posture, particularly weak patients, should support their legs against a wall. The entire process of this *mudra* should not take more than five minutes.

Come back to the rest position and stay for a few moments and then perform the following asanas each for 2 to 3 times: *Shalabhasana, Bhujangasana, Ardhachakr-asana* and *Hastpadasana*. Those who are sick and weak should instead do *Yogamudra, Pawanamuktasana* and *Shalabhasana*. A strong and relieving motion follows within 10 minutes after practising these asanas.

This process of easy evacuation ensures perfect cleaning of the bowels, so that all impurities in the stomach or the intestines are washed out with water. Neither enema nor any laxative is capable of performing this task so thoroughly and so naturally as this method is capable of doing. Sometimes decomposed bile and acids stick inside the walls of the intestines and the stomach and become the cause of many diseases. This method gradually dilutes them and passes them out of the body along with the water drunk in the morning. The asanas suggested in this method quicken the process of this dilution as also quick, easy and natural evacuation. It is so safe that even the sick can practise this.

Common Diseases and Suggested Asanas

Common diseases and the suggested asanas for their cure are given in the following chapter. It should again be emphasised that this does not give complete yoga therapy. These asanas can safely be practised without any harm whatsoever. Women however should stop practising *yogasanas* after three months of pregnancy and during menstruation periods. It has been seen in many cases that they produce wonderful results in the very first week of their practice. It is therefore necessary to do them with faith, devotion and proper technique. Diet control is also a must.

❏❏

14. Cause and Cure of Diseases

To stay healthy is our birth-right. To obtain this right it is not necessary to take help of medicines, but to stay healthy is in our own hands. As explained earlier the structure of human body is so made that it functions like administrative system of a country. Various parts of the body perform different functions. One of the systems of the body performs functions of defending the body from disease by keeping immune system functioning properly. Just like external aggression is blocked by defence forces and rest of the national life is directed to support the defensive efforts. In the similar manner, any infection or toxin getting in the body is repulsed by immune system activating the blood cells and other toxin expelling mechanisms to get rid of the infection or disease bearing bacteria.

For example in a fever blood-pumping is increased by higher pulse-rate, body gives a feeling of fatigue and requires rest and there is loss of appetite. Body needs rest and noise of T.V. & family irritates. In case we help the body by resting, reducing intake of food, by restricting to water & lime in couple of days fever can be got rid of. Similarly various fundamentals about curing the diseases need to be understood and followed to stay healthy.

Meaning of Good Health

To stay healthy we have to direct our energy inwards rather than wasting it on external comforts and enjoyment. We are looking for cures etc. from outside the body and in today's polluted environment it is becoming more difficult. स्वास्थ्य means available within our body and yoga teaches us to activate such mechanisms located inside the body. Nature has made the human body so complete that it is possible to stay healthy by keeping the internal systems working properly and in co-ordinated manner.

The body falls ill due to many reasons, main reason, as per modern science, is harmful bacteria causing infection or a disorder. But ailments caused by mental stress etc. have no

166

physical basis and are caused by mental stress etc. All functions of the body are controlled by brain through complete nervous system. With mental stress function of all systems is impaired and ailments start attacking the body and vicious circle of medicines and re-actions starts.

Ill Health is Caused by Carelessness

The main reason for bad health is incorrect food and over-eating. To give energy to body, keeping the blood stream clean, and all organs to function in alert manner depends on our food habits. Incorrect food, imbalanced food, over-eating irregularly and being a compulsive eater cause diseases to creep in the body.

Yoga experts and naturopaths believe that accumulation of toxins in the body causes various ailments. Bacteria germinate where toxin or unclean areas are located causing diseases. In case we pay attention to this fact, before disease attacks, we can achieve good results.

It is not possible to achieve good health by any medicine invented or likely to be invented. The method to stay healthy is within reach of every human by activating internal organism. Regular use of a medicine can reduce the activity of internal organism to the extent of being ineffective and result in complex diseases. Medicine, therefore, when taken should be minimum & for minimum period to cure an ailment and then aim should be to improve immune system by controlled diet, exercise and cleaning process. The medicine can act to augment internal system only when the systems are working properly. If it is possible to be healthy by consuming drugs and chemicals, then no one will fall sick, so long as he can buy the medicine. But this is not possible. We have to practice and find our own method to stay healthy by balance of type of food, rest & exercise.

There is slight misconception about achieving good health through yoga. Widely published and therefore believed concept is that an ailment or a disease can be cured by one particular yogic posture or a combination of postures. It must be understood that yogic postures have not been designed keeping any disease in mind, but make internal organism to function properly, removing toxins and achieving good health. It is a step to have good immune system and robust constitution. By regular practice of yogic posture body stays

167

healthy because human structure is designed in such a manner that tends to stay healthy naturally and yoga keeps this process active.

It has not been possible, even by latest research, to identify exact cause of sudden bouts of ill health, like loose motions, acidity, running nose, cough, skin diseases etc. Presently the causes of diseases are said to be infection, allergy, bacteria and virus. But it is strange that affect of these causes is not the same on all human beings. A person with low immune system is likely to fall ill earlier. Excess use of medicines also results in low immunity level. It is therefore, essential to improve immune system so that, an organism in the body function at their optimum level. Regular practice of yogic postures, cleaning processes, *pranayama* and meditation makes the body supple, mind calm and defense mechanism of various systems active. The yogic method is therefore, best way to stay healthy.

Cure or Giving Rest to Body

The main aim of any therapy is to give rest to the body and calm the mind and the methods used may be naturopathy, or by changing the diet pattern. This will help the inbuilt defensive system to fight the disease.

Most of the ailments or ailment generating elements get eliminated by fasting and one feels well. The fasting can be by use of water-honey-lime, warm water, fruits/vegetables, juices. Boiled vegetables and salads can sustain a man for weeks. Milk and curd can be added as well as juices of vegetable & fruits. Some cereal may be included after some time, but with brawn i.e. roughage. Green leafy vegetables may be mixed in flour for *chapatis*. Carrots, bottlegourd, white gourd, cucumber & citrus fruit, juice with lime & honey is very useful and its consumption for 3/4 months cures even chronic diseases.

Grapes, raisins, big raisins (मुनक्का) and honey combination is very good for lung infections like T.B. & asthma. Cough & cold gets cured by the juice of ginger and amla mixed with honey & hot vegetable soup. For dysentery & diarrhoea apple/pomegranate juice & ripened banana are very good. For relieving joint pain take soaked garlic, ginger and raisins, carrot-ginger and vegetable-juice and soup.

CLASSIFICATION OF DISEASES

It is the law of nature that toxins are expelled from body by oxygenisation in lungs, perspiration and calls of nature i.e., urinary & excreta tract. Whenever the natural toxin throwing passages don't work properly various ailment start appearing. Largely the diseases can be in three categories.

1. Acute Diseases
2. Chronic Diseases
3. Degenerative Diseases

Acute Diseases

As the name indicates such ailments are with acute discomfort/pain e.g. high fever, loose motion, dysentery, cold, cough, skin diseases, smallpox, cholera, etc. Such diseases occur in children and adults with low resistance capabilities. They occur to throw toxins from body and last for 3-4 days and some for one to two weeks and as soon as toxins are expelled the ailment subsides. Even if no medicine is taken and food consumption is restricted and regulated, the disease subsides.

In food carbohydrates and proteins should be avoided. Consumption of proteins and carbohydrates initiate digestive cycle and interrupts cleansing process. The medicine can suppress the disease, but there can be relapse as soon as as effect of medicine wears out.

In acute diseases consume only water for 3-4 days and then add sweet fruit juices and vegetable juice/soup. Patient should take complete rest. Do not exercise or perform any yogic postures. As the disease subsides, appetite improves and body is cleaned. A little weaknees follows, which improves slowly.

Chronic Diseases

Such diseases continue for long periods, although patient continues to live & work but is in very great pain and suffers continuously. Pain in joints, gout, asthma, diabetes, stone in kidney/gal bladder, urinary infections etc. are included in the list of chronic diseases.

To cure such diseases a patient should fast for a week, consuming only water with lemon and honey and juices of fruits & vegetables. For next three weeks, only fruit & vegetables juices & raw salads be consumed. The vegetables like cucumber, bottle gourd, spinach, carrots and white pumpkin be used for juices. A cup of milk and cheese may be added. After about two months boiled vegetable and about two *chapatis* can be consumed for one meal and the remaining meals should include only juices, cup of milk. The sequence may be repeated till the disease subsides.

While curing the chronic diseases the target is not the disease but improvement of body resistance systems. Exercise recommended postures, cleansing process & *pranayama* be performed regularly. This routine will improve the resistance power and immune system. Patients should be advised to relax & stay cheerful.

Degenerative Diseases

When chronic diseases are not cured properly or are suppressed by medication then degenerative diseases may appear. Such disease start eroding the body e.g. cancer, heart ailments, T.B. etc.

Degenerative diseases should also be treated by consuming minimum and easily digestible food, like recommend for chronic diseases, but for longer duration. The starting by complete fasting, however, is not necessary, and treatment can start with juices and small quantity of milk.

It must be remembered disease is indication that body is trying to expel toxins from the body. Acute diseases when suppressed by medication cause avoid chronic ailments. In case of chronic diseases strength of the defensive systems in body should be improved by using five basic elements earth, water, air, fire and space.

All efforts should be directed to avoid ill health and in case of one falls ill, cleansing process should be initiated. It is better to follow yogic life of exercises, food, cleansing process, clean air & sunlight, rest and stay tension-free & cheerful.

CURE OF AILMENTS BY YOGA

The practice & yogic posture is not aimed at cure of any specific disease, but suggests comprehensive way of life to stay healthy. However attempt is being made to list out common ailments & recommended postures to cure them. Along with exercise & cleaning processes suggested foods for specific ailments are also listed in this chapter.

Constipation

When suffering from constipation one should avoid food prepared with fine flour as base and all dishes which involve deep or shallow frying. Consume food having roughage like *Atta* with brawn, whole pulse (not washed), leafy vegetable, salad, guava, papaya, pears, wood apple (Bel) & Citrus fruits. Consuming water, kept over night in a copper container, first thing in the morning is specially recommended.

Among exercises, *Suryanamaskar, Ardhamatsyendrasana, Makarasana* and *Pawanamuktasana* are very useful.

In cleaning processes Kunjal (self induced vomit) and enema may also undertaken.

Piles

A patient with piles should consume food suggested for constipation, concentrating on vegetable juice and restraining completely food which can irritate the piles. Apply *oil on piles with help of finger inserted inside the rectum.*

Paschimottanasana, Yog Mudra, Gorakshasana, Makarasana, Sarvangasana and *Agnisar Pranayama* can be very useful.

Gastric Trouble

Eat easily digestible food by chewing each mouthful properly. Leafy vegetables like *Palak, Bathua* and *Methi* be made in to paste and added to dough for *chapati* and kept for 8-10 hours before cooking. Eat dry *chapatis* without consuming any water with it. Take warm water after about half an hour. At night take only milk and fruits.

Paschimottanasana, Ardhamatsyendrasana, Vajrasana, Suptavajrasana, Makarasana, Pawanamuktasana, Halasana, Uddiyanabandh and *Agnisar Pranayama* are very useful postures. Nauli and Kunjal performed at regular interval can also be useful.

Obesity

While bathing scrub the body for 10-15 minutes with small and slightly rough towel. At night patting with palm, closed fist and dry massage will activate the fat cells. In the food reduce quantity of Carbohydrate & Proteins and add fruits, vegetables, juices, and fat free milk/curd.

Suryanamaskar, Naoasana, Suptavajrasana, Sarpasana, Mayurasana, Uttanpadasana, Paschimottanasana, Makarasana, Halasana, Uddiyanabandh and *Agnisar Pranayama* are useful postures.

Seminal Disorders

Massage, sun-bath, scrubbing the body while bathing. Eat light and limited food and add milk, curd, cheese and fruits. Milk should be sweetened with dates in place of sugar.

Paschimottanasana, Gorakshasana, Ardhamatsyendrasana, Suptavajrasana, Dhanurasana, Halasana, Sarvangasana and *Uddiyanabandh. Nadishodhan Pranayama* and retention of the breath after inhaling are recommended exercises.

Diabetes

Brawn added atta for *Chapatis, Methi, Karela* and *Palak,* vegetable salad, *jamun* and fruit juices can control the diabetes. Two-three flowers of *Sadabahar* is useful preventive method.

Paschimottanasana, Makarasana, Uddiyanabandh, Yogmudra, Ardhamatsyendrasana, Suptavajrasana, Uttanpadasana, Mayurasana and *Nadishodhan Pranayama* are helpful postures.

Ear, Nose & Throat

Lime and honey in warm water. Tea made of ginger, green cardamom & pepper and light food is suggested.

Ushtrasana, Bhujangasana, Halasana, Sarvangasana, Matsyasana, Jalneti, Sutraneti and *Kunjal* followed by *Bhastrika, Bhramari & Ujjai Pranayama* will give good results.

Liver Diseases

Food should be without any fat and have vegetable & fruit juices, with honey & lime juice with honey will also be helpful.

Kamarchakrasana, Paschimottanasana, Ardhamatsyendrasana, Yogmudra & Halasana among yogic postures, *kunjal* as clearing process and *Sheetli* as well as *Uddiyanabandh* as breathing exercise will be helpful. Perform *Yogmudra* 8-10 times daily.

172

Asthma & Lungs Diseases

It is common belief that asthma is a lifelong disease. A strict vigilance of diet is very necessary for an asthmic to lead normal life.

One or two *chapaties* having brawn and leafy vegetable, boiled vegetables and salad should form the meal. Take lime warm water with honey, soaked raisins or मुनक्का. Tea of cardamom, ginger & pepper or पीपली, tulsi leaves and मुलट्ठी may also replace tea etc.

Among asanas perform *Suptavajrasana, Ushtrasana, Bhujangasana, Shalabhasana, Makarasana, Jalneti, Sutraneti & Kunjal* should be done every day. *Kapalbhati & Bhastrika* are recommond *Pranayamas*.

High Blood Pressure

Salt and spicy especially chilly based food is to be completely stopped. Patient should try to stay on juices, soups and fruits, fat free milk, curd & cheese. Food should by light minimum possible.

Kamarchakrasana, Vajrasana, Suptavajrasana, Sarpasana, Bhujangasana, Shalabhasana, Uttanpad-asana, Makarasana & Pawanamuktasana, should be performed and when proficiency is reached add *Sarvangasana* as well. *Kapalbhati, Nadisodhan* (without retention) *Pranayamas* will be useful. Practice *Shavasana* for 10 minutes couple of times everyday.

Low Blood Pressure

Warm lime water & honey, soaked almonds & raisins, milk, cheese, fruits, salad should form part of light food. In addition to *Suryanamaskar* (कर्णपीठासन) all asanas, mentioned for high blood pressure, should be performed.

Headache

To clean the internal passages perform *Kunjal* and fast by consuming small quantities of fruits & milk.

Paschimottanasana, Tadasana, Bhujangasana, Halasana, Sarvangasana, Shavasana, Kapalbhati & Nadishodhan Pranayama will be helpful.

Dislodged Navel

Dry *Chapati*, curd, boiled vegetable, *khichari*, apple & bannana should be consumed.

Tadasana, Vajrasana, Suptavajrasana, Ushtrasana, Uttanpadasana, Dhanurasana, Matsyasana followed by *Uddiyanabandh* will be very useful.

Cervical Spondylitis

Take light food, avoid gaseous food and include fruits in diet.

Suptavajrasana, Ushtrasana, Bhujangasana, Dhanurasana, Uttanpadasana, Tadasana, Makarasana & Matsyasana followed by *Shavasana, Nadishodhan & Kapalbhati Pranayama* is recommended. Perform *Bhujangasana* 8-10 times daily.

Hernia

Never overeat. Constipation condition should be avoided. Keep the bowels clean. Food should include vegetables, fruits, but avoid gas producing food.

Paschimottanasana, Yogmudra, Ardhamatsyendrasana, Suptavajrasana, Uttanpadasana, Pawanamuktasana, Halasana & Sarvangasana to be performed, avoid other postures.

Heart Diseases

Take vegetable & fruit juice, lime juice and honey in fresh or warm water. Try to sustain on vegetable/gram soup & skimmed milk for as many days as possible. Take light food and in small quantities every 3-4 hours. *Chapati* with brawn and leafy vegetables and vegetables can be added after sometimes.

Start with light exercise like walk at slow pace and short duration. Add *Kamarchakrasana, Vajrasana, Bhujangasana, Shalabhasana, Uttanpadasana, Makarasana* and *Pawanamuktasana*. Keep your capacity in mind. Take rest after the asanas by staying in *Shavasana* for 5 minutes. *Nadishodhan pranayama* should be done, without retention, and as per individual capacity.

Rheumatic Diseases or Gout

Food for patients is similar to that given for asthmatic patients.

Yogmudra, Vajrasana, Suptavajrasana, Uttanpad-asana, Bhujangasana, Makarasana, Pawanamuktasana, Sarvangasana & Matsyasana should be performed upto individual capacity *Bhastrika Pranayama.* Sunbath and massage followed by warm water bath will be very useful.

Sleeplessness & Other Nervous Disorder

Keep bowls clean. Increase intake of fruit, fruit juice & milk.

Among the asanas, perform *Suryanamaskar, Paschimottanasana, Ushtrasana, Makarasana, Dhanurasana, Halasana, Sarvangasana,* and in *Pranayamas Sheetli, Kapalbhati* and *Nadishodhan,* followed by *Yognidra* for half an hour. Avoid sleeping in the afternoon and practice early rising.

Kidney Trouble

Consume liquids which are non-toxic and non gas-forming. Lime water with option of honey, vegetable & fruit juice. (Citrus fruit and pomegranate). Ginger & Cardamom tea for few days. After a while have good food once a day and remaining time non-toxic liquids.

Practice *Yogmudra, Ardhamatsyendrasana, Uttanpadasana, Suptavajrasana, Bhujangasana, Dhanurasana, Makarasana, Pawanamuktasana, Matsyasana, Uddiyanabandh, Bhastrika Pranayama & Kunjal.*

Menstruation Disorder

Include fruit juice & vegetable juice especially carrot, cucumber & vegetable salads in your food. Do not allow constipation to set in. Refrain from greasy & sour food.

Janusirasana, Paschimottanasana, Gorakshasana, Suptavajrasana, Yogmudra, Uttanpadasana, Makarasana, Dhanurasana, Uddiyanabandh, Agnisar, Kapalbhati Pranayama and *Kunjal* will be helpful.

❑❑

175

Suggested Daily Routine

Getting Ready

1. *Pawanamuktasana* (Exercise for 9 joints), *Bhastrika* (during winter), OM (three times), GAYATRI MANTRA.

Warm-up

2. *Suryanamaskar* (Salutation to SUN), Nao (Boat) & *Kamarchakra Asana* (Spine Rotation).

Asanas While Sitting

3. (a) *Paschimottana* (Forward Bend)   (b) *KON* (Angle)
   (c) *Ardhamatsyendra* (Spine Twist)   (d) *Vajra* (Hardy)
   (e) *Ushtra* (Camel)   (f) *Suptavajra*
                                                  (Horizontal Hardy)

   (g) *Shashank*

Asanas while Face Down

4. (a) *Sarpa* (Running Snake)   (b) *Bhujanga* (Cobra)
   (c) *Shalabha* (Locust)   (d) *Dhanura* (Bow)

Asanas while Face Up

5. (a) *Hala* (Plough)   (b) *Tara* (Tree)
   (c) *Hastapadottana*   (d) *Makar*
   (e) *Uder-Pawanamukta*   (f) *Dolan*
   (g) *Sarvanga* (Shoulder Stand) (h) *Matsya* (Fish)

Cooling Down

6. (a) *Singh Garjna* (Roar)   (b) *Laughing*
   (c) OM   (d) *Kapalbhati*
                                       (Active Exhalation)

   (e) *Uddiyana Bandh*   (f) *Agnisar* (Pumping
      (Retention out)   the stomach)
   (g) *Pranayama*   (h) Eye Exercise

Additional Routine

7. (a) Cleaning processes   (b) Yognidra
   (c) Meditation   (d) Resting

❏❏

Laughter
The secret of good health

—S.P. Sharma

The fastest way to break the ice in many a situation is to crack a joke. Which is why Danish pianist Victor Borge quipped: "Laughter is the shortest distance between two people." This book is replete with humorous one-liners, quips, quotes and anecdotes that will have you doubling up with laughter. The book also dwells on famous humorists and other personalities with a sharp sense of humour, including Mark Twain, George Bernard Shaw, Oscar Wilde, Winston Churchill, Abraham Lincoln and Mahatma Gandhi, amongst others.

Jokes apart, laughter also has multiple therapeutic benefits, as attested by renowned doctors. Indeed, in March 1995, the first Laughter Club was lanched by a Mumbai-based doctor precisely for the therapeutic benefits. This book also tells you all about the scientific benefits of laughter. So read, laugh and be merry. For therein lies the secret of good health and happiness.

Demy Size • Pages: 120
Price: Rs. 60/- • Postage: Rs. 10/-

You are What you Eat

—Tanushree Podder

How your body responds physically, mentally & spiritually to your food hab

Did you know that food could heal, cure, elevate moods, improve memory, make the brain sharper, provide us with potent energy and fill us with vigour?

Food has been discovered to be the greatest natural pharmacy tha' is available to human beings. The right food can help us perform t(our peak capacity while the wrong food can lead us towards diseas(and ill health.

The ordinary cabbage and cauliflower could ward off the possibilit of cancer, tomatoes can effectively take care of free radicals i today's environment and carrots can provide you with the essenti beta-carotene to fight off many diseases. It is surprising ho effectively food can alleviate most of our common ailments.

The mysteries of the power of food and the secrets of food elemen have been unravelled so that you can use food for other benefi rather than just appeasing hunger.

Demy Size • Pages: 184
Price: Rs. 80/- • Postage: Rs. 15/-

YOGA for HEALTH

—*N.S. Ravi Shankar*

Yoga today is universally acknowledged as a natural way to sound health and overall physical and mental well-being. And given its popularity a variety of self-help yoga guides are available to the reader. But what makes this book unique is its approach and presentation. The book packs over 100 yogic asanas thoroughly illustrated, and backed by well-designed techniques to perform specific exercise from first step to the last with each explanation followed by the Therapeutic advantages of that posture. From how Tadasana gives strength to legs and feet and stimulates nervous system, Garudasana removes cramps in calf muscles, Natarajasana helps to reduce fat, it goes on to explain the benefits of Ardha Chandrasana in strengthening digestive system, of Vatayanasana in curing joint pain, to list a few.

In addition the book offers an overview of this age-old science, besides a detailed index of different ailments and the names of asanas useful in curing them. A special chapter is also devoted to specific yogic exercises for Farmers, Pregnant women, Aged people, Artists and Craftsmen, Models, Students, Executives and Sportsmen.

Big Size • Pages: 184
Price: Rs. 96/- • Postage: Rs. 15/-

The Joy of Natural Living

—Luis S.R. Vas & Anita S.R. Vas

The Joy of Natural Living incorporates research findings on health, psychology, body care and spirituality which emphasise the benefits of natural living. A common theme runs through all the material gathered here. —the more you rely on nature and nature therapy in dealing with your physical and mental problems, the more joy you get out of life.

The authors hope the reader will be able to regain natural joy by experimenting with some of the advice from experts presented here which include:

✦ Coping with stress through relaxation techniques and Pleasant and Positive thoughts.

✦ Role of diet in achieving mental & physical well being.

✦ Safe & successful physical activity program.

✦ Natural grooming and herbal preparation to attain increased self-confidence

---

Demy size, Pages: 152
Price: Rs. 80/- • Postage: Rs. 10/-

Sure-n-Safe
Weight Loss Programme

—Pankaj Sharma &
Dr. Ashok Gupta

T his self-help weight loss book is probably India's *first well-defined programme on losing weight positively and naturally.* The book includes information on other weight loss regimens in the market and discusses their pitfalls.

Following the *Safe-n-Sure Weight Loss Programme* also ensures you don't regain the lost weight after some time. This step-by-step programme includes an exercise regimen and crucial information on food and diet, with an exclusive chapter on low-calorie recipes, vegetarian as well as non-vegetarian. All of which makes this book a truly hosistic weight loss guide that will help you lose weight *safely* and *naturally,* and *maintain* your ideal weight thereafter.

Demy Size • Pages: 132
Price: Rs. 96/- • Postage: Rs. 10/-

Diet in Diseases

—*Sunita Pant Bansal*

Diet plays a crucial role in promoting or preventing a disease. Especially when down with a disease, simply swallowing pills will not prove as effective if dietary guidelines are ignored. The appropriate therapeutic diet can speed up the recovery process and even boost the immune response. However, diet is one aspect of therapy that even doctors many a times fail to give due importance to. Simply put, over-nutrition, under-nutrition or wrong nutrition must equally be avoided if one wishes to stay slim, trim and fighting fit.

This book lists an array of ailments and conditions and outlines the right diet that could cure or control these problems. Once you begin having balanced, sensible meals, it won't be long before you kiss goodbye to those pills. This book will show you how to eat right and stay fit.

Demy Size • Pages: 104
Price: Rs. 69/- • Postage: Rs. 15/-

Healing Power of FOODS

—*Sunita Pant Bansal*

Nature's Prescription for Common Diseases

Hippocrates, the father of medicine, recognized that the medical therapy must be consistent with the nature and the design of the human body. He believed that the effective health care could not be separated from nutrition. He stressed prevention of disease by strongly recommending a balanced diet with a moderate and sensible life style. Hippocrates wrote, "Natural forces within us are the true healers of disease... Everything in excess is opposed to nature... To do nothing is sometimes a good remedy." His philosophy was very much akin to the holistic health perspective of today.

The various foods provide not only nutrition to our body, but can prove to be medicinal too. 'Healing power of Foods' introduces all the main food groups to the reader, giving details about the medicinal uses of the commonly used foods from these groups. The tips given are simple, practical and effective. The healthy recipes at the end of the book complete the role of the various foods in providing nutritional as well as medicinal benefits.

Demy Size • Pages: 136
Price: Rs. 60/- • Postage: Rs. 10/-

Reversing Aging

—*Dr. Bruce Goldberg*

Aging slowly allows us to enjoy life to the hilt, rather than expend our energies resisting Father Time. The very thought of growing old and the inevitable difficulties usually associated with aging depresses most people. Now science is on the threshold of showing us how aging can be prevented, or at least delayed.

Reversing Aging presents both theory and specific techniques to deal with life's challenges associated with aging. The author, Dr. Bruce Goldberg, has drawn the most accurate and useful information available from the fields of personal grooming, gerontology (the study of aging), nutrition, exercise, biochemistry and alternative medicine to help improve and retain your vigour throughout life.

In the book, you will discover:

❖ How to use self-hypnosis to slow down the aging process.
❖ How to take a balanced diet for a longer life.
❖ How to change your lifestyle to preserve youth.
❖ How to change aging indicators.
❖ How to look younger through simple, natural methods.

Demy Size • Pages: 216
Price: Rs. 80/- • Postage: Rs. 15/-
